The HAIR book

The HAIR book

By celebrity hairstylist ANDREW BARTON

NEW
HOLLAND

First published in 2010 by
New Holland Publishers (UK) Ltd
London · Cape Town · Sydney ·
Auckland

Garfield House
86–88 Edgware Road,
London W2 2EA, United Kingdom
www.newhollandpublishers.com

80 McKenzie Street, Cape Town
8001, South Africa
Unit 1, 66 Gibbes Street,
Chatswood, NSW 2067, Australia
218 Lake Road, Northcote,
Auckland, New Zealand

Text copyright © 2010
Andrew Barton
Photographs copyright © 2010
New Holland Publishers (UK) Ltd,
except those listed on page 175.
Copyright © 2010 New Holland
Publishers (UK) Ltd

Andrew Barton has asserted his
moral right to be identified as the
author of this work.

ISBN 978 1 84773 763 2

Publisher: **Clare Sayer**
Special photography: **Emily Bell**
Production: **Laurence Poos**
Design: **Fiona Andreanelli**
Editorial Direction: **Rosemary
Wilkinson**

10 9 8 7 6 5 4 3 2 1

Reproduction by Pica Digial Ltd,
Singapore
Printed and bound by Times
Offset(M) Sdn Bhd, Malaysia

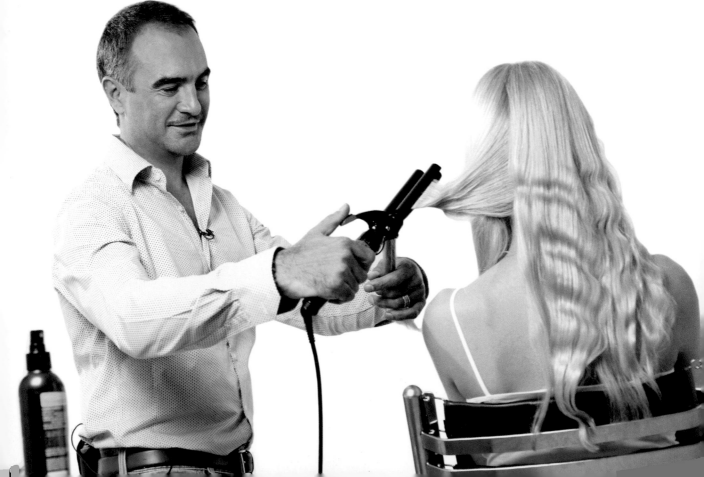

I would like to dedicate this book to those (too many to mention) who have supported and encouraged me throughout my work and life – yes you know who you are. Special mention goes to my amazing team at Andrew Barton Group, my wonderful mother and family for caring and to Vitali for believing that our dreams do come true!

CONTENTS

When a woman has
Shiny Happy Hair,
EVERYTHING
is possible

About *About* Andrew Barton

Writing this book has been a great experience and has really made me think about how I feel about hair and why I am where I am now. I call it my hair addiction. Every day I work with hair and so I'm always aware of the potential that good hair has to transform how a woman looks and feels; how it can excite and ignite her emotions and give her a sense of power and the feeling that she can conquer anything in her path. When a woman has Shiny Happy Hair everything is possible, nothing stands in her way and her life is truly ON! She walks tall and is proud to flaunt her crowning glory! She's in control!

It is witnessing (and bringing about) this display of happiness that inspires me when I design and create hairstyles and has probably spurred me on to where I am today. I thrive on it! I guess that's the thing about good hairdressers – they see hair as art, as design, as something that can transform. A hairstyle doesn't have to be radical or extreme or even necessarily in fashion, but if it's right for the wearer then it can speak volumes. I'm literally addicted to the smile I see when a woman sees herself in the mirror when I've finished her hair. I can make a woman look taller, slimmer and younger with the right hairstyle. But it's not just about technical skill or being a good designer – it's about having the know-how and the experience. My career has been a wonderful journey – I've scoured the world in the pursuit of hair knowledge, tried and tested countless products and gadgets and explored every hair myth. All this so I can tell every woman the secrets to having **Shiny Happy Hair!**

> I guess that's the thing about good hairdressers – they see hair as art, as design, as something that can transform.

I'm often asked how I got into hair and what it feels like to be a lad from a small mining village in Yorkshire who has ended up as 'TV's favourite hairdresser'. I certainly started small time – it's not quite a rags-to-riches story but I certainly came from humble beginnings. As they say, from tiny acorns mighty oaks grow!

It all started with my mum taking me to the local salon while she had her weekly 'do'. The very smell of the place excited me. I would play with my building bricks in the corner as mum leafed through the latest copy of *Woman's Own* under the hood dryer at 'He and She' – the local unisex salon in the village. My mum and grandmother were there every week at the same time, transforming themselves from the working class ladies that they were to the Hollywood starlets that they read and dreamed about. In my eyes my mother looked like a young Elizabeth Taylor – all raven glossy locks – so

the hairdresser didn't have to work too hard to turn her into a divine vision of beauty. Each week she left that salon looking fabulous, each week a different 'look' depending on whether her hair had been flipped or coiled or teased. I was amazed! Those rollers and sprays, teases and tweaks made my eyes wide with amazement as I stared in disbelief at the wonder of what was being created. I'd stare in the mirror speechless as my own hair was cut, not missing a snip or a flick of the stylist's wrist or brush. At home I would spend hours combing every hair on my head into place, only for it to be rained or buffeted by those harsh Yorkshire winds as soon as I left the house, or scuffed up by the school bully. Meanwhile I'd scrutinize the hairstyles of my aunts or my mother's friends – deciding what looked good and what didn't. At school my artistic side was nurtured by my art teacher, Gwen, who was fresh from teacher training

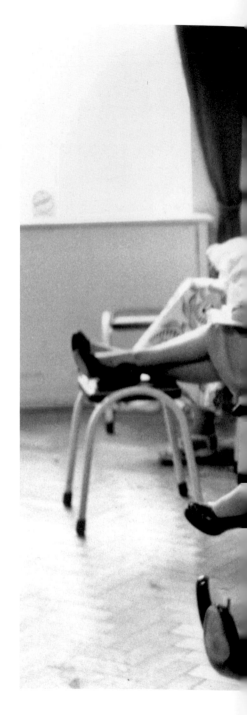

Who could have imagined that years later I'd be standing on stage in front of 3,000 hairdressers in Beijing cutting the hair of a top model with **paper scissors** to achieve a blunt cut bob!

college and full of encouragement for those of us with creative leanings. She was ready to change the world with her enthusiasm. My brother's hair, my sister's 'Girl's World' (not to mention her Sindy, Barbie and Tiny Tears) didn't stand a chance. Come to think of it, neither did she! I learned how to plait, discovered the wonders of gels and hairsprays – I even cut hair with paper scissors! Who could have imagined that years later I'd be standing on stage in front of 3,000 hairdressers in Beijing cutting the hair of a top model with paper scissors to achieve a blunt cut bob! Fashion darling!

When the time came to leave school I decided I was destined for fashion college and so off I went. However, I didn't stay long as the magnetic pull of the salon was just too darn powerful! I started hairdressing in a small village salon that had a huge reputation. My mother insisted if I wanted to be a hairdresser I had to learn from the best and the best around at that time was Denise Moody. I was petrified of her (moody by name, moody by nature, maybe). Her standards were incredibly high, everything was done in a certain way and tea was served on fine bone china. The word 'OK' was not allowed! We, her staff, stood to attention as she arrived at work, ready for a hard day's slog. Broom in hand, I would do my best to impress. As I rinsed every bit of lather away, I'd dream of becoming as good as her; as I cleaned her tools and made her lunch I would take every opportunity to watch her like a hawk so I could pick up her every move. She was glamorous, travelled to foreign places and had shag pile carpet. I loved her! I was determined to prove that I could and would make it to the top! As I listened to her telling clients of her trips to Acapulco I knew I had to travel too, and see what lay beyond the mines and moors of Yorkshire and learn more about women and their hair.

So one day I packed my bags and jetted off to Australia, Asia and the USA to do just that. In Sydney I learnt how to do the perfect sun-kissed beach highlight, in New York how to give the Manhattan 'blow out' and in LA how to surf and do hair all in the same day. In Bangkok I tressed for those who loved to show off their wares on pole dancing stages in the red light district. But London was too much to resist and, in true Dick Whittington style, I believed the streets were paved with gold and I'd become the hairstylist on everyone's speed dial. And more or less, I did!

I've been blessed to work alongside stylists from Brazil, France, Spain and Italy as well as the Londoners who have all shared their know-how. I swear I was like a sponge – absorbing every last drop I could learn about women and their hair. I've sweated backstage at the leading fashion shows of the world, from London, Paris and Milan to New York; sat around for hours waiting for celebrities to allow me into their dressing rooms and been ushered into palaces to tend to royalty; appeared on daytime television talking about the latest trends and made countless women look *10 Years Younger* on the hit make-over show of the very same name.

> I've been described as a 'saviour', a 'saint', a 'hero', an 'angel sent from heaven above' all because I can transform a woman's hair.

It's a far cry from my humble beginnings but I've loved every glamorous minute: the glitz as well as the long days, hours of travelling and demanding divas (and there have been a few, I can tell you). I'm a hairdresser who loves doing hair and creating magical transformations. Catwalk, salon, magazine shoot – it doesn't matter. As long as I'm doing hair, I'm in heaven. My dream has come true!

My reputation as one of the world's leading hairstylists has led me to the four corners of the world. I've been described as a 'saviour', a 'saint', a 'hero', an 'angel sent from heaven above' all because I can transform a woman's hair. I'm booked up months in advance and recognised in the street. I'm trusted as the beauty journalist's first point of call for all things hair, whether it's *Vogue* or *Cosmopolitan*, the tabloids or broadsheets or the TV chat show sofa. So I decided it was high time to write the definitive hair book and share all of my knowledge, secrets and know-how with you.

With my own brand of haircare, electrical tools, hair extensions, brushes and hair accessories much of my life is now managed by my team and I guess you could say I've got it pretty easy now. But in spite of having the endless help and support of my PA, PR, MD, CEO, agent, trainer, publicist and my dear editor, and even after being crowned 'British Hairdresser of the Year', what I love doing most is hair. There will always be new frontiers to cross, more for me to learn and share. As long as hair keeps on growing, I'll be happy because I can feed my addiction, my addiction to transforming women and giving them *Shiny Happy Hair!*

Andrew Barton x

Introduction

Hair can be transformed in a 1001 different ways.

From the subtle to the spectacular, a haircut can sum up your personality and make a huge difference to the way the world perceives you, from glamorous to casual, trendy to classic, cared-for and nourished or – heaven forbid – dirty or damaged. Hair has huge religious, cultural, traditional and iconic significance. It can say more about fashion and time that any magazine article, and can bring forth powerful emotions, from tears of sadness to tears of joy and everything in between. And achieving Shiny Happy Hair is a life time pursuit for many!

HAIR IS AN EXPRESSION OF PERSONALITY, INDIVIDUALITY AND RANK.

Hair has a language of its own. The way it's worn, arranged and dressed reveals something of the owner's identity. Hair is an expression of personality, individuality and rank. Hair has created rebellions, controversy, pain and joy!

Most of us have our own hair habits and it's the easiest thing in the world to get stuck in our ways (hair straighteners, anyone?) Throughout this valuable book I'll share with you all there is to know about your addiction. They say it takes 21 days to break a habit; it might take you a little longer to break your bad hair habits, but break them you will! Hair can be a security blanket, like wearing baggy clothes if you're overweight. You sit in disbelief and fear as the hairdresser snips off your hard grown inches thinking quite literally that the sky will fall in! Or you dream of a new life, a new love or just that a slimmer, taller, fresher, sexier you will emerge from the clouds of spray and puffs of mousse.

Hair is exciting and ever-changing, hair is the object of ritual and adulation, magic and transformation! The difference between a good and a bad hair day is full of psychological drama and inexplicable emotional behaviour. Mother Nature may have given you a head of fine delicate strands or a thick lion's mane but you ignore sensible advice and insist on pulling, ironing, tweaking and torturing your hair into submission – all in the name of fashion and beauty, expectation and making the right impression. I see women flinch when they pass a shop window and catch sight of the slightest sign of frizz, believing they are on the edge of a disaster. Cosmetics companies and magazines conduct countless surveys about natural beauty and, although it sounds good in theory, most of us want to improve on what we were given naturally. You wouldn't choose a lipstick that was the same colour as your lips, so why would you pick a shampoo to give you flat lifeless hair? It's all about enhancing what you have and making the most of the best bits. Throughout this book you'll find plenty of advice on how to do just that.

Hair is erotic and provocative. Long flowing hair has always been associated with vitality and sexual allure. A lock of hair from a beloved, captured in a locket, is the ultimate romantic gift and symbolizes intimacy. Celebrities transform their images and careers (and consequently their earning power) with a new hairstyle. Rapunzel used hers to allow her lover to climb up the tower to be with her. Letting down one's hair in front of a lover can be very erotic and is an invitation for intimacy. Most men are blissfully unaware of the world of straightening irons, serums, conditioners and other tricks women use to transform their locks but show a man a woman with beautiful, sexy, glossy hair and he will always notice! The women I meet are smart, sensible, sane individuals who know that great hair gives them great power – power to be the women they want to be and have the life they want to lead. They devote much of their waking hours thinking about, looking after, touching, checking and obsessing about their hair. And why the hell not? It's the outfit you never take off, the one thing that can transform your whole appearance. If you have Shiny Happy Hair – it's envied!

I've had clients who have talked to their shrink, their hypnotist, their doctor, their mother, their priest – even their gynaecologist about their hair! Hair is important to every single one of us.

Hair can say so
many *different* things

Vain

Classic

POWERFUL Mythical

Rebellious

Iconic **Romantic**

INFAMOUS

Biblical *Magical*

Re-invented

Contemporary

For decades rock legends, pop stars, movie icons, supermodels and royalty have understood the powerful effect hair can have – and many of them know exactly how to manipulate this obsession with hair to their advantage. From Marie Antoinette with her fantastic and elaborate wigs in the eighteenth century, to Marilyn Monroe, Debbie Harry, Princess Diana and, of course, the ultimate reinventor, Madonna, people have endlessly speculated about what it really means to turn heads with your hair. I could write whole chapters on the social and cultural effects hair has had over the centuries but I'll save that for another time. Instead I want to share with you how to achieve the holy grail – Shiny Happy Hair. Along the way, I hope you'll learn a little more about your crowning glory!

Whenever I do someone's hair, I'm aware that it can be a decisive moment. A snip here, a spritz of sweet-smelling spray there – I have the power to control destiny! A visit to the salon, whether it is in your local high street or at a glittering Manhattan address, can be many things: a ritual, an escape, fun – part of our lives. For many the hair salon is the centre of the community. That magical time at the hairdressers allows you to escape your realities and luxuriate in your hair fantasies – we call it hair porn!

Back at home in your own bedroom, sitting at your dressing table or standing in front of your bathroom mirror, there's no reason why you shouldn't be able to recreate some of the salon experience. Tackling your locks may be fraught but it can also be fun. Sometimes hair is a joy, sometimes it's a nuisance. I've spent many an hour in the company of women as they sit and discuss their hair and for a few moments they escape everything else in life and think only about themselves. Hair is special to us all!

When you can give yourself the time, there's nothing better than high-maintenance hair. I call it high-heel behaviour. You know when your hair looks great, you walk taller and with a spring in your step; it really is a confidence booster! I know that in reality most time-poor women want hair that is low maintenance – who doesn't want to look their best in the least possible time? But all I'm saying is that if you're in a hair rut and your hair isn't doing it for you, perhaps a little time spent reading this book will help you achieve your dream – **shiny happy hair!**

"There's no such thing as an ugly woman, *just a lazy one*"

Helena Rubinstein

Shiny Happy Hair doesn't come easy – unless you have been blessed with fantastic hair genes. Great hair comes down to a number of different factors:

Genes Colour Texture Shape

Length Styling **Potions** Tools

With a little know-how, a bit of practice, the right products and just a few more minutes a day you really can make a huge difference. *Trust me.*

The science bit

Throughout this book I want you to
understand more about your hair and
why it does the things it does, often without
any logical explanation. So let's start with
the science!

Hair is a complex mix of

keratin (a protein found in nails, feathers and horns), as well as water, carbon, oxygen, nitrogen, hydrogen, calcium, iron and two types of lipids. I know – wow! A single hair has many stories to tell and chemical analysis of hair is used for medical, legal and environmental purposes to find clues for illness and crimes alike. For a forensic scientist it provides a wealth of information and in the nucleus of each hair bulb lies the complete information of a person's genetic inheritance, found in the form of your DNA. So the next time you are cursing your hair for misbehaving or hurriedly blasting it with 200 degrees from a hairdryer, just give it a little more thought and respect.

Hair does not grow continuously throughout life but in successive cycles of approximately three to ten years. The cycles have three stages: growth, regression and loss. At any one point in time around 85% of your hair is in the growth phase and 15% is in the loss phase. So there is no need to be alarmed when you see hairs in the bath tub or on your hairbrush. On average we lose up to 100 strands of hair a day – that's just the 15% that's in the hair loss phase. If our hair cycles were synchronised we'd moult regularly like some animals.

Much of the hair fibre is invisible to the naked eye and the layer that we see is known as the cuticle. If you were to look at it under a microscope it would look similar to overlapping roof tiles in appearance. These scales are held together by lipo protein cement. When the condition and quality of the hair is compromised, the cuticle scales (roof tiles) are lifted instead of lying flat and the cement that secures them together is lost. Shampooing, and particularly conditioning, helps to lay those tiles back down and cement them back together. Many of the more sophisticated hair care brands have special ingredients that work just like the cement. You'll often read on the back of a shampoo bottle all about repair, proteins, lipos and cement actions – it is baffling sometimes but basically this is exactly what it refers to.

Much of the hair's other characteristics, its colour, shape and texture (what I call its personality, determined by your DNA) is housed in the inner layer of the hair, the cortex. Colourants, perms, relaxers and some conditioning agents set to work on this inner layer to change the DNA personality of your hair for a longer lasting result.

Heat styling and blow-drying only works on the outer layer (the cuticle) and therefore these effects are only ever temporary. Which is probably a good thing – you probably wouldn't want to change your hair's personality so easily!

And now the final 'science' question: is your hair dead or alive?

Technically when each individual hair pushes its way through your scalp from the hair follicle, it is dead material. The hair fibre is no longer nourished by the living tissue that manufactures it. The tip of each individual hair on your head has seen a lot of wear and tear, and the longer the tip the older the hair. You should bear this in mind when selecting haircare products: long hair may benefit from some of the anti-ageing haircare products around as technically long hair is aged hair. Like any material, the older it is the more delicate it becomes and the more it is affected by what you – as well as the elements – throw at it. Styling, heat exposure, chlorine, salt water and brushing all take their toll on your hair and therefore it needs lots of TLC. Fortunately for you ladies, modern haircare can offer solutions and remedies to help you achieve optimum hair health.

How to
FEED
your hair

Each hair grows approximately 15 mm (half an inch) every month and has the capacity to keep on growing longer and longer for anywhere between three and ten years.

Some of you may find your hair will grow to your waist, while others find that frustratingly, your hair barely grows past your shoulders.

Much of this depends on your hair's DNA. We generally inherit characteristics from one side of our family's makeup and I often hear clients say how they've got their mother's skin but their father's hair. But other factors can play a part in how much hair you have and how long you can grow it. Wear and tear, stress and general poor health are never going to be good for your hair but nutrition plays a surprisingly large part. Damage from heat styling will not slow down the growth of the hair but it will make the ends weaker and therefore prone to splitting. This kind of damage to the ends of the hair is easy to identify as it is clearly visible. However, hair grows from the roots so it's not always possible to see what the problems are. Nourishing your hair is what really matters and no amount of fancy products and quick fixes is going to make a difference to how your hair grows.

The root, or hair follicle, is the incubator of hair growth and is nourished by our blood supply. For years I have been singing the virtues and benefits of eating a healthy, balanced diet, taking plenty of exercise and drinking lots of water – all as a way of achieving Shiny Happy Hair. I can tell at a glance when my clients have been taking care of themselves and when they haven't – even all those celebrities who have an army of helpers to keep them fit, healthy and beautiful can sometimes neglect the most basic things. Their hair can tell me a million stories. I know when they've been burning the candle at both ends, not going to the gym and forgetting their diets and certainly when they are under a lot of stress. When the body is under attack or feeling the pressure the first place it takes essential nutrients from is the hair and skin – it's the front line, if you like. The food we eat really does make a huge difference to the essential nutrients that hair needs for growth.

Serums, potions and lotions will cosmetically help the hair to look and feel better but they are just quick fixes. Getting to the root of the hair is much longer-lasting and more effective! With these basics under your belt, the easier it is to achieve Shiny Happy Hair.

You can surely tell a lot about someone from the health of their hair. Neglected, damaged hair lacks shine and is lifeless – splurging on this season's fashion must-haves and applying layers of fabulous make up can never disguise dreary, dull or disastrous hair. Dandruff, excessive oiliness, dryness and hair loss can all be identified as SOS signals.

On the other hand, Shiny Happy Hair tells the world that you eat a good balanced diet with plenty of fresh fruit and vegetables, enjoy a healthy lifestyle and take some form of exercise. We all know what's bad for us (alcohol, smoking, junk food, late nights, stress) so it doesn't take a genius to work out that cutting down on these nasties is better for our hair too. If it's beautiful locks you yearn for then a diet check may be in order! No, I didn't say go on a diet to get Shiny Happy Hair, just keep an eye on the nutritional content of the food you eat.

When we eat, our bodies go to work breaking down the nutrients. The hair and scalp need these nutrients as much as any other part of the body – in particular vitamins A, B, C and E. And don't think you can cheat by taking a vitamin supplement – it may help a little but the real thing is what the hair needs! So here's a checklist of what foods are good and bad.

What's *in*

citrus fruits
strawberries
leafy green vegetables
soy beans
nuts
seeds
coconuts
sprouts
mackerel
tuna
eggs
garlic
pumpkin seeds

What's *out*

junk food
sugary drinks
mucus-forming foods, especially dairy products
   (but hooray low fat cottage cheese is in)
excessive amounts of animal fats
high levels of wheat
refined white bread

The path to *Shiny Happy Hair* is certainly not paved with fad diets – it's about achieving a balance and making sure you eat regularly so that you body gets a good intake of nutrients. Replace chocolatey snacks and crisps eaten between meals with some delicious fresh fruit and your hair will thank you for it.

Fish is a fantastic source of protein and, eaten regularly in a balanced diet, produces much of the protein the hair needs. In particular, oily fish (such as mackerel, tuna and salmon) are rich in Omega 3 – and these essential fatty acids are great hair boosters. Omega 6, another winner, is found in walnuts, flax seeds and sesame seeds, so fill up your basket the next time you go to the health food shop! Coconut is a miracle food for hair, encouraging shine and strength. Other shine-enhancing foods include cabbage, broccoli, garlic, onions and pumpkin seeds.

Shiny Happy Hair needs up to eight glasses of water per day

Water is totally and utterly the fountain of life and Shiny Happy Hair needs up to eight glasses per day. Water cleanses the system, hydrates the body and provides fantastic moisturizing qualities for your hair.

So far so good? There's more – salads, fruits and vegetables and plenty of water will not give you all the nutrients your hair needs. As mentioned before, hair is a protein so eating protein is vital. Add eggs, fish, chicken and occasional lean red meats to your diet and you'll soon see the Shiny Happy hair effect!

Of course, everyone's metabolism varies and some people will notice the difference more quickly than others. Patience is a virtue and it may take time to see those results – but believe me, you will! I always think improving the diet should be the first step but I know that there are also plenty of vitamin and mineral supplements – and some of them can be very effective. Talk to your pharmacist or health food specialist to see if they are right for you.

THE PERFECT
Shiny Happy Hair Meal

BREAKFAST

You know how everyone says that breakfast is the most important meal of the day? Well it really is! Try:

eggs, salmon, ham, kippers or low-fat cottage cheese

low-fat cereals or yogurt

wholemeal bread with honey

fresh fruit

LUNCH

Don't be tempted to skip lunch – the likelihood is that you will end up snacking on something naughty mid-afternoon!

mixed fresh salad or grilled vegetables

fresh grilled fish or chicken

fresh fruit or yogurt

DINNER

This can be difficult if you like to go out in the evening. Occasional glasses of wine and treats are allowed! Keep carbohydrate portions small.

wholemeal pasta or rice

salad or vegetables

fish, chicken or lean red meat

VEGETARIANS

Protein is essential for strong healthy hair so vegetarians should be aware that they need to find protein in other ways.

Defining your hair's
'PERSONALITY'

What I mean by personality is really what
we professionals call texture. Most of us
know whether we have thick or thin hair
but knowing how best to treat your
hair type is the key.

'My hair has a personality all of its own!'

I hear you cry. If I've heard that once I've heard it a thousand snips. Well, let's make a little more sense of that. Hair is best described as falling into one of three categories and once you know which you have it certainly makes it a lot easier to understand its erratic behaviour and make it do as it is told!

It is important to remember that your natural hair texture can change and is affected by all sorts of things including the weather, your health, pregnancy and how many children you have. And of course, let's not forget the ageing process which (sorry to alarm you) actually starts in our early thirties. Throw in other factors such as whether you colour your hair, use heated tools, spend lots of time in the sun or go out when the air is humid and you shouldn't be surprised when your beautifully blow-dried straight locks turn into poodle frizz – bad hair day! Hormones change hair growth and texture and as your hormones are all over the place during and after pregnancy this has a huge effect on hair. It's all down to the individual and what affects one woman's hair may not affect another's. The same goes for grey hair. Some women end up with a coarse yard brush, while others can have silver hair that's silky, soft and smooth. Thyroid problems can cause hair loss and a complete change in hair texture. So yes, hair really does have a mind, a will, and a way all of its own!

Many of the clients that visit me are trying too damn hard to achieve the impossible in the name of fashion. Take the girl who has gorgeous natural curls and spends hours straightening it, only to find that she can't go outside the front door in case the slightest bit of humidity turns her beautiful smooth tresses into frizz – devastating! And who wants to be a slave to the iron? Then

'We always want what we haven't got'

97.5 g   3.4

there is the woman who dreams of big hair but can't achieve it without half a can of hairspray. And who wants to run their fingers through that, my dear? Whether I'm talking to a celebrity or not, I always try to get my clients to embrace what they have and get the best from it, rather than have a life of hair torture. Understanding and accepting what your hair's personality is is the first and biggest hurdle. You probably know better than anyone else what your hair texture is and how it works and what it will and won't do! Take a good, hard, long look in the mirror and work out which of these best describes your hair texture. By correctly identifying your hair texture you will ensure that you are well armed to make the right decisions when buying shampoos, conditioners and styling products and when choosing the best hairstyles.

There are only 3 main hair types:

1 Fine
2 Medium
3 Thick

Fine hair is the thinnest of strands and is therefore the most delicate. Having fine hair doesn't necessarily mean that you have less hair – you might have lots of hair on your head but of a very fine texture. Fine hair can be curly, wavy or straight. Fine hair is no more difficult or easy to style than other types of hair and believe me, fine girls, I've got plenty of thick-haired clients who'd love to have your locks. There are loads of gorgeous fine-haired women out there – *just look at* Cameron Diaz.

Medium hair is the darling of hair textures. It is easy to manage, easy to change and you can pretty much do anything with it. It can be straight, wavy or curly and if you have it, consider yourself blessed. *Jennifer Aniston*, who probably had the most requested hairstyle of recent times, is a classic medium hair texture girl.

Thick hair has good and bad points. Envied by those who don't have it and cursed by those who do, it can be more challenging to look after. If it's straight, it's much harder to curl and if it's curly you can end up with an unruly mess. On the plus side, thick hair often grows longer and more quickly and feels healthier. *Sarah Jessica Parker* is a typical thick-haired girl.

So, whatever your hair texture, there are pros and cons. To achieve your goal of shiny happy hair it is important to pick the right products and every haircare regime should start with the most vital ingredient – the shampoo.

What is shampoo?

Shampoo is a chemical mixture blended with all kinds of goodies to clean the surface of the hair and the scalp. A lot of the time these blends feed the outer layer (the cuticles) with moisturizers to help those cuticles lay flatter and reflect shine. It is true that shampoo does take away some of the natural oils that your scalp produces but don't be alarmed by this. These oils only gather at the root area and the first couple of centimetres of the hair so the drier, older areas of your hair would never benefit from these natural oils anyway. It is the ends of your hair that need the moisture so it is much better to use a gorgeous, cleansing, moisturizing shampoo to do the job. If anything, natural oil left in the hair will result in oily roots and dry tips. Shiny happy hair certainly starts with clean hair free of oils. What the shampoo washes away is replaced with something altogether more beneficial. A good-quality shampoo and conditioner used in harmony will leave the hair feeling fresh, clean, smooth, shiny and easy to style.

So whether you wash your hair every day, which you probably do if you have fine or medium hair, or once a week if it's thick, is not important – it's all about what's right for you and how you do it!

Choosing the right shampoo can be the fun part and makes all the difference to managing your hair personality.

The formulation and technology of shampoos is constantly changing and improving and modern products are a far wash away from the first shampoos. Believe it or not, shampoo was only invented in the early twentieth century. The word shampoo is derived from the Hindi word 'chhampo', meaning to massage or knead. Today's shampoos are beauty treatments in themselves. We often judge the quality of a shampoo by the way it lathers – and it's true to say that the lather is all-important when it comes to how much you enjoy using it. It usually just demonstrates the levels of detergent. There will often be more lather on the second shampoo as the residue of oils and pollutants are washed away. Shampooing your hair is a bit like preparing your skin for make up; fresh clean hair reacts much better to styling and generally helps to hold styles for longer.

Dry shampoos are a fabulous way of making your hair last another day if you don't have time to wash it. Usually in an aerosol or powder formula they are sprayed or sprinkled at the roots and absorb the oils of the day making the hair feel fresher. For those of you with fine hair, they have an added benefit of adding a little more volume and give the hair a thicker feel. Dry shampoos are the secret weapon of many a celebrity and my kit bag wouldn't be complete without them.

In the nineteenth century hot water was believed to soften the hair but was reserved for the wealthy.

For most people rapid washes in cold water was the method used along with lots of brushing and combing to clean the hair. Perfumers sold various crèmes, pomades, oils and powders to disguise dirty hair but the first shampoos were used at hair salons.

Shampoo Myths

1 Will scrubbing my hair harshly clean it better?

No. Scrubbing with pressure will aggravate the scalp and encourage it to produce more oil thereby creating an oily scalp – death to a blow-dry or any style.

2 My grandmother always said a hundred brush strokes a day was good for the hair. Was she right?

I'm afraid Granny had this one wrong. Overbrushing your hair will put pressure on the very fibre of the hair and encourage it to split or tear! Only ever brush dry hair not wet and brush gently to avoid tears.

3 Does using really hot water make the hair cleaner?

There is some truth in the idea that warm water helps to open the outer layer of the hair fibre but generally using hot water will parch the hair and scalp just like the skin. Instead always use warm or tepid water.

4 What about rinsing in cold water?

Ignore this one as well – apart from making you cold (brrr!) it can also constrict the blood capillaries that carry nutrients to your hair's growth cycle.

5 Should I regularly change my shampoo? I've heard that hair can 'get used' to the same shampoo and stop working.

I don't believe this one – there's no need to buy detox shampoos or switch brands all the time. If you want a quick detox for your hair and scalp, simply leave the lather in your hair for a few extra minutes before rinsing.

People often ask me how often they should wash their hair. The answers are usually always the same: it's up to you to decide how often your hair needs washing. Much depends on your hair's texture and personality, as well as your lifestyle and environment. Fine hair usually needs to be washed more often than thick hair but it also makes sense to me that as we wash our faces every day, we should probably wash our hair as often!

Should you spend or splurge on a shampoo (and its partner, conditioner)? There is certainly a lot to be said about the weird and wonderful array of products out there, from caviar extract to bull's sperm. I've tried them all and while some have certainly made the hair feel lovely others have not been so successful. We are all much more aware of environmental issues now and buying organic products is high on the agenda for many of us.

You may want to make an ethical decision when it comes to your shampoo. But all said, shampoos are essentially cleaning agents and you need to consider that when you are enticed by all the wonderful marketing claims. Many of the leading super brands do have amazing research facilities – I've visited many of them and I've certainly been impressed with the know-how and research that goes into how a shampoo effects the tensile strength of the hair and its elasticity. Many of these brands have founded great technology and patented their formula. One ingredient to look out for is Dimethicone. It's a silicone and appears in most shampoo brands to some degree and its efficacy can have great results for shine. However, the higher up the ingredients listing it appears the more negative the effect it can have on the hair. These negatives include creating a barrier that colour and heat styling cannot penetrate evenly or consistently, so beware of low-budget brands that use these ingredients liberally.

Look for shampoos and conditioners that have all the hallmarks of the professional brands which include concentrated formula, active ingredients and a great fragrance – you want to enjoy using the product. For instance, in my own signature range I have added shea butter as an active ingredient for moisture.

There is something to be said for the psychological benefits of using more expensive brands and therefore if you find spending lots of cash on a shampoo works for you – stick with it. Remember that brands that are sold at the salon are accompanied by years of knowledge and advice and there's a lot of value in that.

Now that you know a little more behind that little bottle of shampoo in your shower, what's the best way to shampoo? There is an art to it – just think how wonderful your hair feels when it's been washed at the salon. Many of my clients say that's the best bit, so use this as a starting point and think of washing your hair as a ritual.

shampoos are essentially cleaning agents and you need to consider that when you are enticed by all the wonderful marketing claims

The cheaper brands are generally nothing more than cleaning agents, while the luxury labels have the added benefit of more active ingredients added. I think the best advice I can offer is that a medium-priced product will do a perfectly good job, as there are so many other factors that come into play in achieving shiny happy hair.

There are some simple rules to follow and remember an – extra minute spent caring for your hair at this crucial preparation stage can make all the difference.

Step 1 Before wetting your hair, comb out any tangles with a wide-toothed comb. Start at the tips of the hair and work up to the roots.

Step 2 Soak the hair with warm water, gently stroking the fingers through your hair as the water flows through it. The type of water can also affect your hair in different areas. For example, soft water can leave the hair feeling lank while hard water can make the hair feel brittle. Fitting a water filter to your tank can make a huge difference by making the hair more controllable. Luxury salons often fit water filters for this reason.

Step 3 When the hair is wet through, gently squeeze out the excess water.

Step 4 Pour a teaspoon-sized blob of shampoo directly into the palm of the hand. Rub the product together in the palms of your hands then smooth the shampoo over the hair. Gently rub your palms over your head and then build up a little more pressure on your scalp using your fingertips. Don't scratch your scalp with your nails. Continue this process for approximately 30 seconds, running your fingers through your hair evenly to avoid tangling.

Step 5 Rinse, rinse and rinse again! It's important to rinse away all those lovely bubbles. Not rinsing away the residue of the shampoo thoroughly enough results in dull hair.

Step 6 To repeat or not? If you are washing your hair daily there is no need to shampoo twice but if you like the feel of super clean hair, shampoo and rinse again.

Conditioners

Conditioning your hair is an essential part of the process to achieving shiny happy hair. A conditioner smoothes the outer cells of the hair (the cuticle) and therefore avoids individual hairs tangling. The added benefit is that conditioners align the cuticle scales and therefore make hair feel softer to the touch and encourage shine. Earlier in this chapter we mentioned the three main hair textures: fine, medium and thick. For thick-haired girls there is rarely such a thing as overconditioning but fine-haired girls often have a dilemma with conditioners for fear of losing body in their hair. This is likely if the conditioner feels heavy. Instead opt for lightweight, gel or spray-based conditioners rather than rich creams. Body is reduced when the offending conditioner is not rinsed out of the hair thoroughly. This is why leave-in conditioners only tend to be good for girls with thick hair.

Most importantly, conditioners put moisture back into the hair, so that it looks and feels nourished. Never underestimate the moisture lost from the hair from constant styling abuse. You would always moisturize your skin and hair is just the same – it really does benefit from conditioner.

Just like shampooing, applying conditioner is a bit of an art form. It should always be applied to clean, washed hair. Follow these simple steps:

Step 1 Squeeze the hair firmly to remove excess water after the final rinse of shampoo.

Step 2 Pour a teaspoon-sized blob of conditioner into the palm of your hand, rub the hands together and smooth the conditioner over the hair avoiding the roots and paying attention to the tips.

Step 3 A well-formulated conditioner does not need to be left in the hair to work and should be rinsed out straight away. Use warm water and run your fingers through your hair to make sure it is thoroughly rinsed. There are, of course, deep conditioning treatments and masks that have the potential to penetrate deeper into the hair's cells, thereby repairing more structurally than cosmetically. These should be left in the hair for longer, but for most hair textures these only need to be applied once a week.

After allowing yourself the time to complete this hair pampering ritual in the shower or bath, the next stage is to gently squeeze out the excess water from your hair. I've seen so many girls rub their hair madly at this stage – all this will do is tangle the delicate fibres and make the hair feel rough. Use a wide-toothed comb (I recommend my 'Andrew Barton No Knots Comb') to comb your the hair so it is ready for styling.

So far so good? Shiny happy hair does mean time. I'm often asked what's the best hair tip I can give and it's always about spending a few more minutes on your haircare, whether it's massaging our scalps a little longer or rinsing those gorgeous perfumed bubbles away for a few more seconds. Time is such a commodity and because of this women often rush through their haircare routine and feel frustrated with the end result. Just applying a weekly deep conditioning mask can make a huge difference to how your hair looks, feels and behaves. Beauty is totally in the eye of the beholder but how you feel about your hair can boost your confidence and make you stand out in a crowd.

STYLING
your **hair**

Your mother probably told you that when you have to work so hard to make something happen, it's probably best to let it go – whether it's a relationship, a job or an unrealistic hairstyle! Most of the hair problems women tell me about are to do with their locks not doing what they want. The trick to great hairstyling is to embrace some of your hair's natural texture (personality) and enhance the rest. A lesson with your super-duper hairdresser will help you learn some tricks of the trade.

You can sizzle

and fry your hair into submission as long and as much as you want but how long the effect will last is another question, only to be answered by the heavens above. It's essential that when you style you use a properly mixed cocktail of products and that cocktail depends on your hair's texture (personality). I usually work a mixture of three products into hair when I style, all chosen for their lightweight clean feeling in the hair. I always start off with a liberal spritzing of heat protective spray (like my Andrew Barton Straight Answer Hot Iron Protection Spray). Apply evenly throughout the hair and then add the following styling products, depending on your hair type.

Fine hair
80% mousse to 20% smoothing crème and a fixing spray to hold.

Medium hair
50% mousse to 50% smoothing crème and a fixing spray or serum to define and hold.

Thick hair
80% smoothing crème to 20% mousse and a serum to define.

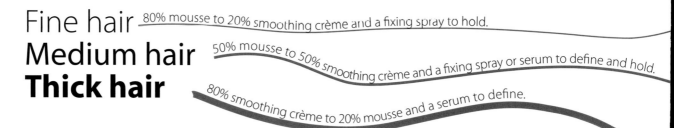

These formulas will work whether you want to make your hair straight, curly or wavy or whether you want to add or decrease volume. It's all about texture control.

Don't be confused by all the hype surrounding miracle styling products. A good regime of the appropriate shampoo, conditioner, deep conditioner and the styling products mentioned above are all you need. Less is always more when it comes to good products. Many people are scared of styling products but used sparingly and in the right place they are your hair's best friend.

What to use where?

Smoothing crèmes should be applied mainly through the lengths and ends and not at the roots.

Conditioner is mainly used at the lengths and tips – never the roots.

Heat protectors can be applied throughout the hair.

Scrums should only be used at the tips. They can temporarily seal a split end.

Mousse can be applied throughout the hair.

Of course there are times when styling just isn't necessary and in fact, spending hours making your hair look gorgeous would be downright silly. Think of those wonderful carefree days at the beach or on holiday, letting your hair blow wild and free while your feet sink into soft sand. There's nothing better! All you need to do is coat your hair in conditioner, whip into a bun, plait or under a very cool hat and enjoy styling downtime! Because the rest of the time, if you want to look your hair best, it's all about styling up time!

The market is awash with styling products and tools and no doubt so are your bathroom cabinets. It's no wonder most of us are confused so in order to make things a little easier for you I thought I'd empty out my kit bag and share the key basics of a good capsule hair kit...

My top summer hair tips

Do not squeeze lemon juice on your blonde hair. Lemon juice is highly acidic and will fry your hair to total dryness and only add brassy yellow tones.

Contrary to popular belief, sunlight will not make your coloured blonde locks blonder. UV light will fade blonde hair colour so to avoid a washed out look and hair that looks dull, keep your blonde hair covered up in the sun – pop on a gorgeous sunhat.

A heat protective spray works wonders at keeping your hair nicely moisturized and will help prevent unsightly frizzing. My Andrew Barton Straight Answer Hot Iron Protection Spray has a gorgeous holiday fragrance so your hair will smell lovely too.

Use a hair mask when on the beach or spending long days in the sun – simply rinse out at the end of the day. The mask will add moisture and make your hair beautifully soft to the touch.

The kit bag

1 Water spray bottle for damping down unruly, just-got-out-of-bed hair. For extra moisture you can mix in a little of your favourite conditioner – spray and leave.

2 Heat protective spray. Available in creams, gels and sprays. I prefer sprays as you can direct them more easily and they're light and fresh in the hair. Perfect for all hair personalities.

3 Smoothing crème. A lightweight smoother – great for controlling frizz and humidity.

4 Mousse. The unsung hero of hairstyling, it adds oomph to fine hair personalities and helps to control thicker rebellious hair texture during the torture test of blow-drying.

5 Hairspray. A dry aerosol mist that holds, adds shine and can also double up as a heat protector. It will also give protection from damp atmospheres.

6 Serum. Even the tiniest drop of silicone-based serum can smooth, correct and polish the tiredest of hair.

7 Dry shampoo. A secret weapon for ridding the scalp of oil and making a blow-dry last another day. A celebrity must-have.

8 Kirby grips. Still the best around, these are ideal for securing bits of hair when you don't want them in your eyes or when you are creating a fabulous up-do.

9 Curling tongs. Even if you wear your hair straight tonging the ends of the hair for a pretty look can be a winner. Go for large-barrelled tongs or conical-shaped ones.

10 Hairdryer and diffuser. Diffusers are great for when you want a look that is more tousled and textured.

11 Straightening irons. The must-have item for most girls – perfect for super straight, bends, waves, kicks and curls. The easiest tool around.

12 Velcro or heated rollers. Heated rollers are perfect for glam hair and Hollywood bounce. Use only a few to create gorgeous red carpet hair.

13 Texture crème. For that perfect beach-tousled texture, to add lift or sleek an area down.

14 Hair clips or butterfly clamps for sectioning and securing areas. These allow you to work on one area at a time – just like a pro.

15 Tail comb to help you divide and section.

16 Brushes. Round or flat, covered or vented, the right brush will help you get the style you want.

17 A wide-toothed or jumbo comb. Use in the shower to comb hair through and for detangling.

18 No-snag hairbands for that perfect catwalk ponytail.

19 Hair vitamin or supplement for that deeper care.

20 Last but not least, the right shampoo, conditioner and deep conditioning treatment for your hair's personality.

I know you will be asking – but what hairdryer should I buy? Which brush is best for my hair? Let's start with the big one first.

There are so many hairdryers to choose from. And guess what, they are not that bad after all, and have come along way since their invention. We all know the damage associated with heat styling but can't resist the look that styling gives. Blaming your poor hairdryer is an easy cop out! As with most things in life, it's not what you do it's the way that you do it. Overuse of electrical tools can rob the hair of moisture leaving it feeling and looking parched as an old thatched roof!

Blow-drying is all about controlling your hair's personality. The tools that you need will depend much on the desired result – for instance, your hands may just do the job if you're looking for a tousled, natural-looking do, but if you want your hair to look smooth and sleek or if you want to add volume, then you'll need to use a brush. Paddle brushes work best when you're after something sleek and round brushes are brilliant for volume or pulling out stubborn kinks or bends.

Follow these simple steps for easy hairdrying.

Towel dry as we have discussed before. Never rub but blot instead, removing as much water as possible. You should never blow-dry wet hair – it should be damp. This way you'll find it easier and quicker and it will cause less heat damage to your precious locks.

Always use a styling product cocktail as we've discussed suitable for your hair's personality.

Choose the right tools. Use brand names you trust and know or that have been recommended to you.

Choose appliances that have speed and heat controls – you'll never need more than 1500 watts and use the nozzle to concentrate the heat, flow and your effort.

It makes sense to blow dry the back and sides first. Over 70% of the hair is distributed at the back of the head and you'd never leave the house with the front of your hair looking a mess, would you? Most of the bad styling I see on the streets (sorry, occupational hazard) is when the back has not been styled. Keep the nozzle approximately 15 centimetres (6 inches) away from your hair. Start blow-drying on a higher temperature and reduce the heat and speed as the hair dries. Hair gets burnt by repeatedly going over the same area, drying out the moisture content in the hair cells. This results in dry, brittle broken hair. Using a nozzle on your hairdryer helps to direct and concentrate the heat and therefore results in quicker blow-drying.

Tip your head upside down first and blast the hair, this gives the roots a lovely lift. If you want to create even more lift, body, wave or curl than your hair has naturally, clip sections or roller them to the head. As you dry each section allow the hair to cool into the new shape you have created, then take the clips or rollers out at the end when the hair has cooled.

Using heated rollers can take a lot of the strain out of blow-drying. Take random large sections around the head and put in the rollers. Applying the rollers in a random way will give a natural effect; putting them in horizontally will give more lift and putting them in vertically will create a cascading effect. Allow them to cool for ten minutes while you finish your make up, take them out and give your hair a shake or brush through – now you're ready to go!

Once the hair is dry there may be other heat styling choices you want to make to complete your style, for example straightening irons or tongs. If handled incorrectly there are many dangers associated with their use and the increased chance of frying your hair, so follow these simple rules:

- Do apply another layer of heat protector.
- Do not hold a tong or iron on your hair for more than a few seconds.
- Do not continue going over the same area time and time again. This is the most damaging thing you can do.

And if it's technology you are after or you are bombarded by the bewildering choice out there, then here are some easy-to-understand terms:

- **Ceramic** These generally have more durability than metal or plastic and retain the heat better as well having an even temperature. Ceramic technology can be found in hairdryers, irons, tongs and even brushes and reduces the chance of the hair snagging during the straightening process, especially in irons, tongs or brushes.

- **Titanium** Again, titanium technology is very durable and conducts heat evenly. The titanium is computer-designed for a precision heat-controlled system.

- **Ionic** There is much scientific debate about ionic technology and the explanation is based around the reduction in the size of the water droplets during the drying process, enabling quicker drying. Ionic technology also has the added benefit of reducing static during the drying process.

- **Touraline** This is a natural mineral substance that when built into the mechanics of a hairdryer, tong, iron or even a brush, can speed up the drying process.

In general terms the other benefits that you should look for is something lightweight and with a professional label. Professional tools have usually benefited from many of the scientific breakthroughs mentioned above, thereby reducing the damaging effects to your hair and helping you to achieve *shiny happy hair*.

So, we've discussed styling products, we've examined heat appliances, what about brushes? Can a brush make so much difference to the quality and control of your hair? Yes, indeed it can!

Brushes come in all shapes and sizes and by laying bare my kit bag I hope to have helped you navigate the choice that's out there. Brushes and combs have a long history and have been around for thousands of years. When it comes to natural versus plastic, my rule of thumb is you probably need both. Natural bristles tend to be softer as they are less prone to damage and wear and tear and therefore do not snag the hair fibre. Plastic bristles are great heat conductors which make them easy to use for quick blow-drying. Coupled with a metal barrel the hair can be blow-dried and shaped into your desired look very easily. Use natural bristles when the hair is dry and plastic when the hair is being dried from damp. Brands like Mason Pearson, Monroe Margaux, Denman and of course my own shiny happy hair range are renowned for their quality and durability and have won copious awards.

A paddle brush is perfect for straight or smooth blow-drying and speed drying.

A vent brush or cushion brush is perfect for shorter cuts.

Round brushes are the best for achieving volume or taking out curls, waves, bends or kicks.

Bristle brushes are best for dressing and styling the hair into place.

Some of the scariest moments I've seen are brushes coming out of my clients' handbags, looking more like old garden rakes or shaggy dogs. Keep your brushes clean and free of hair to help them do their job properly and achieve *shiny happy hair*.

Getting the
PERFECT
haircut

Hair grows and so must be cut, snipped, carved and chopped! A haircut can turn someone into a walking piece of art.

In fact, haircuts are **influencers** themselves. It only takes the right **celebrity** to randomly **cut their locks** and a **trend is born**, and an army of **looky-likeys** storm the streets.

We all have stories of haircuts we loved having and those that we grimace with embarrassment and laughter about. The history of haircuts is a fascinating journey through woman's independence and revolution. The humble bob cut started life as a rebellious symbol for women's liberation and was considered morally objectionable, to the point where it was discussed in parliament. Haircuts create column inches and can make and break careers. Many of the women whose hair I have cut have carried tiny folded-up pictures of their dream haircut around with them for years. I could write pages about the power of the haircut and how it has changed society but what you really want to know is how to get the best haircut, what will suit you and what to ask for. Armed with a little knowledge you can definitely get the best cut for your *shiny happy hair!*

If it's a crop, a bob or a layered cut you will need to have your hair trimmed every two months, give or take a week. Sure, there are those of you who can make a haircut last longer but the fact is the ends of the hair start to fray, split and tear so even the tinniest of nibbles will make the ends feel thicker and stronger.

I hate to tell you girls there is only one cure for split ends and it's the snip!

Serums can cosmetically disguise those tell-tale signs, but left alone those splits right at the ends of your hair will continue their journey of wreckage. It is tempting when you are trying to grow your hair to avoid the snip snip of the hairdresser's chair but trust me: follow my guidelines on feeding your hair and have a tiny snip every few months and Rapunzel-like locks will be yours.

I know having Edward Scissorhands lurching at you with his silver shears is enough to make you run to the hills and many women quite literally have a fear of hairdressers but for many the hair salon is a place of magic. I love it when my clients say 'I trust you'.

I love it when my clients say 'I trust you'

Different hair textures react to being cut in different ways and it's true to say that the experienced hairdresser has a wealth of knowledge, techniques and tools to deal with your hair's texture. When I'm working in the salon each new cut is a bespoke work of art. I left school wanting to be a fashion designer and that's exactly what I became a fashion designer in hair. Just like a tailor I look for the best features a woman has and try to exaggerate those.

I know that curly hair is often best cut dry rather than wet and fine hair can benefit from being cut with a razor. Thick hair cut randomly can fall beautifully instead of like a bush. My scissors are just a pencil for me to sketch the perfect design for the woman sitting in front of me. If you want shiny happy hair, getting the right cut is just as important as good nutrition, great products and proper styling.

Always insist on a consultation when you visit the salon and if possible talk through what you want without the hairdresser's cape around you – they need to see who you are. If you usually wear make up, don't go barefaced. When a hairdresser says 'same as last time?' you know it's time to find a new hairdresser. If one of my clients always has her hair in a certain way, I might suggest tweaking it and subtly changing it according to what is in fashion – similarly a haircut may need to adjust to the seasons or adapt to the changes that occur in the contours of the face and body. One of the biggest mistakes women make is hanging onto the same haircut for too long. It not only makes them look like they're stuck in a time warp, but that they're trying to hang onto the past (more on that in the chapter on anti-ageing).

On or off duty I can't help but stare at women and think how I could improve their hair look. There are basically five things that I'll check out.

FACE SHAPE As we'll discuss further in this chapter the perfect face shape is oval but with hair cut in the right way any face shape can be changed.

PROFILE Large or small features can be exaggerated or disguised and this is the art of a great cutter.

HEAD SHAPE My clients often think I've turned into some sort of healer when I close my eyes and cup my hands over their heads to feel the shape of the skull. Haircutting is about geometry and balance and with the right cut I can reduce or enlarge the size of the head.

LIFESTYLE Even if you have an incredibly busy lifestyle, we all want the same thing – a hairstyle that we can maintain. Low maintenance is key and there's nothing better than a haircut that is easy to manage. But the paradox is that sometimes we all love a bit of high maintance too. There's nothing quite like that 'me' time when you are pampering yourself for a special occasion.

BODY SHAPE Many people think a good cut is all about what's on top but the perfect cut can complement those thunder thighs, balance that big bum or give you curves you never thought you had!

Many woman aren't lucky enough to be blessed with naturally fabulous hair and will go to any lengths (literally!) to achieve shiny happy hair. I know of a TV presenter who brought her Afghan hound to the salon and said the fur was exactly the length and texture that she wanted her cut like! They do say that owners start to look like their dogs but that's taking it a bit far! And there's the celebrity client who brought a picture of herself with a very wonky fringe at the age of six and said that's exactly how she wanted it cut (she was 58).

Trusting your stylist with your mop is an enviable feat and one many woman can spend a lifetime in search of. A new haircut can make you feel energized and alive – even if during the process you were a bag of nerves, gripping onto the chair, not daring to look up in the mirror and feeling dizzy with anticipation and expectation that this just might be the cut that beats all others!

They do say that owners start to look like their dogs but that's taking it a bit far!

Big changes in haircuts can lead to serious life changes – whether it's finding love, resigning from a dead-end job, finding your dream job or simply reinventing yourself. I'm not going to spill the beans on my celebrity clients who have done just that. With the right haircut the journey to salvation can be found and the road to enlightenment can begin, trust me I've not gone all spiritual on you – I'm just reminding myself and you just how good a great cut can make you feel.

Salons can be daunting environments and hair stylists seem to have a language all of their own. Having worked as a manager at many of London's top salons, I assure you I've seen plenty of characters, from the downright rude to the ridiculous. But generally salons are full of professionals who take their craft very seriously and want to make you happy – so happy that you'll tell everyone you know how good they are. Hairdressers are a bit like salesmen in that they sell their goods, their styles, their trends, their products and themselves. But if they get into that little world where they start talking about levels of graduation, undercuts and overcuts, reverse, parallel and horizontal layering, please, please take a word of advice from me and say you don't have a clue what they're talking about. The best hairdressers will talk your language, make you feel comfortable and understand your needs. Pictures are definitely one of the best ways to convey what you want. Hairdressers are visual people and they do what they can to explain to you what is and isn't possible.

If you've not figured out what's right for your hair texture here is a simple guide to shiny happy haircuts.

FINE HAIR PERSONALITY One length or very long layers tend to suit this hair personality. People often think layers will give volume but often they do the reverse making the hair sit flatter and closer to the head. When you add layers you are basically removing hair and this therefore makes the hair skinny! Chances are if you have fine hair the last thing you want to do is put it on a diet!

MEDIUM HAIR PERSONALITY Oh, you were blessed; pretty much anything goes for you. But obviously it depends on your face shape too, which we'll talk about later in the chapter. Layering can be brilliant to give you va va voom hair but longer layers are usually easier to handle than shorter ones.

CURLY HAIR Curly hair can have a wonderful zany personality all of its own and can come in fine, medium or thick personalities. With this in mind I often cut curly hair dry rather than stretching it straight when it is wet. This is so I can see exactly what the curl wants to do – all you curly girls out there will understand what I mean.

THICK HAIR PERSONALITY You'd think that layers would be the way to slim your hair down and give you a smaller silhouette and they can be. But they need to be cut randomly and very softly to avoid giving you even bigger hair. Sometimes cutting hair away from the underneath and leaving it longer on top can remove volume from the hair.

Going for the chop

There comes a time in every woman's life when she wonders whether she should bite the bullet and cut off those long tresses (more about this in the anti-ageing chapter). Taking 10 years or more off with a snip here and a snip there is what I do best! I truly believe that you should only cut your hair short if it's really what you want to do – for many people hair is powerful (remember Samson and Delilah?). Having long hair makes a lot of women feel younger, sexier and more attractive. Hair can be used as a tool of adornment, of provocation and as a sign of vitality. Vitality is a big word for me when I'm consulting women about their hair. If hair looks tired, is hanging down like a pair of old curtains from a centre parting and has no style then it can be terribly ageing. But longer hair that is full of life and well styled can be very youthful.

To *fringe* or not to *fringe*

A fringe can hide a multitude of sins; it can be provocative, very sexy, and an instant way of bringing an old style bang (excuse the pun) up-to-date. But get it wrong and you won't want to answer the door, not even for Interflora. Fringes come in all shapes and sizes, from short and sweet like Joan of Arc to long and side-swept like Brigitte Bardot, and any true rock chic wouldn't be seen without a too-cool-for-school eyelash tickler. There is a fringe for everyone and good salons will offer free fringe trims between cuts. If you are tempted to snip away yourself, go ahead but never do it when your hair is wet and only snip a little at a time.

ANY TRUE ROCK
CHIC WOULDN'T
BE SEEN WITHOUT A
TOO-COOL-FOR-SCHOOL
EYELASH TICKLER

Before you commit to a fringe or a new cut (the one everyone will admire from afar with envy and say through gritted teeth how amazing you look), think about your face shape and what will suit it. Try this simple trick:

- Tie back your hair and stand in front of the mirror.
- Take a lipstick in your writing hand (perhaps not your favourite Chanel number) and trace the outline of your face onto the mirror.
- Draw the outline of your head and neck and – hey presto – your face shape is revealed.

If you have what's best described as an oval face shape you have what's known in the beauty world as the perfect face shape and you can cut and style your hair in almost any way you choose (although the texture of your hair will need to be considered as well). Don't despair if you don't fall into this category – few women do but with some simple rules they can all look equally stunning.

ROUND Soft ruffled layers on top that add height and length to the face are perfect for this face shape. Try wearing your hair sleek through the sides. A short pretty textured fringe is a winner.

SQUARE Side-swept flirty fringes and feathered layers can reduce the angular shape of a square face. If the face shape is squat add a few soft textured layers on the top for a little lift that will lengthen the face.

OBLONG Adding width through the sides combined with a brow-length fringe will reduce the length of the face. Worn full and bouncy is the way to go. Bobs get top marks too – just don't wear them flat to the face.

TRIANGLE These face shapes fall into one of two categories: narrow and slim at the top of the head or slim at the jaw. For those with narrow on the top it's all about getting some fullness up there, so longer sweepy fringes and layers work brilliantly. For those girls with narrow jawlines opt for bobs and mid-length styles that have fullness around the jaw or neckline.

I often have to stop myself from telling complete strangers on the street how great they'd look if only they did this or that.

There are a million and one observations that I make when cutting the perfect fabulous cut and I often have to stop myself from telling complete strangers on the street how great they'd look if only they did this or that to their hair. Call it my desire to beautify! I take into account the hair texture and the face shape but there are so many other things to consider as well. The right haircut can make you look taller, slimmer and indeed younger! Who needs surgery? We all know good hair makes all the difference.

The best advice I can give is to shop around salons for free consultations to see if a new stylist gets what you are about and the style statement you want to make. You need to be sure that they are true designers who talk to you about your features (good and bad) and explain how they can help you make the most of what Mother Nature gave you so you can walk out of that salon with **shiny happy hair**.

HAIR & sex

That's right – hair is sex! Feeling sexy is all about having good hair. Sounds like a very provocative statement but let me explain and I know you'll agree with me and soon see all the telltale signs. I recently attended one of those speed dating affairs, purely in the pursuit of research for this book, and saw all the visual indications of hair and its sexual allure within the space of a few minutes of being there!

Think about it for a minute, how many times do you touch or check your hair in the mirror?

If it's once I guarantee it's a hundred times more than that! Set yourself a challenge tomorrow and count the times – you'll be amazed.

It's like a natural instinct and psychotherapists, scientists and body language experts have proved time and time again that it is part of mating, courting and preparing for sex!

We spend more personal care time on our hair than any other aspect of our appearance. The way our hair feels and looks affects our mood, confidence and our sexual interest.

We remember someone by the style, the cut, the colour or the quality of their hair and describe people through their hair. In courtship we often have fixed stereotypical ideas of what we prefer, whether blonde, brunette or redhead, long and lustrous or cute and cropped. Throughout history hair has been the subject of poetry, literature and art and when you start looking you will see erotic references everywhere, from Degas' painting of a young woman washing her hair to Botticelli's *Birth of Venus*.

Kissing her hair I sat against her feet,
Wove and unwove it, wound and found it sweet;
Made fast therewith her hands, drew down her eyes,
Deep as deep flowers and dreamy like dim skies;
With her own tresses bound and found her fair,
Kissing her hair.

(FROM 'RONDEL' BY ALGERNON CHARLES SWINBURNE)

Silken threads of charcoal black,
Shimmering iridescent plumage,
Let them swallow me up,
Entangle and entwine,
Ensnare my restless feet
And tether me like a hawk's jesses,
Let me drown in her tresses.

(ANON)

When someone attractive to you enters your space the first thing you do is touch your hair and cock your head to one side in a natural instinct that is in itself submissive. Checking your hair is okay and flaunting it at the same time is very appealing. It's a sexual encounter and one that is repeated many times over throughout a relatively average day. We flaunt and caress our hair; we use it to tease and to provoke attention. Our hair is really the only part of our body that we can acceptably touch in a provocative way (in public, anyway). Flipping, lifting, shaking, twirling and twisting one's hair are all forms of sexual seduction. Caressing your hair also releases pheromones into the air so that your very own scent is released. It's as personal as that; just like the fragrance that you wear from a bottle, your hair sends messages to all those around you. Clean, beautiful, fresh and sweet-smelling hair can certainly make you feel confident and ready for action!

In some societies these very subconscious codes are recognised for their sexual allure and therefore are banned. In many cultures and religions women are required to cover their hair and in times gone by shaving the head was the ultimate punishment for an adulterous woman.

If hair itself can't be trusted as a weapon of mass seduction then the colour of your hair has a sexual language all of its own. Redheads are labelled as fiery and wanton, brunettes are known for their forceful, sassy and dominant natures and the stereotypical blonde sex kittens that we see so often on screen, only perpetuate the myth that blondes are passive and submissive.

From Rapunzel to Lady Godiva, long flowing hair has sent a powerful sexual message. It expresses sensuality and

is a symbol of fertility and vitality. On the other hand, women with shorter hair can be seen as more forceful, assertive and independent, and for many this has huge sexual appeal.

Hair and sex are intrinsically linked and flaunted the world over. As a hairdresser I've worked on so many fashion and magazine shoots and almost every starlet I've worked with has used her hair as part of her seduction and sexual allure.

Sexy hair is what I do best and do every day. A snip of a lock here, a blast from the hairdryer there can make all the difference to how sexy a woman can look.

When your hair is 'done' and looking its best, for a while anything and everything is possible! Hair that is flowing, healthy and shiny has sex appeal – there's no denying it!

The way women use hair as a tool of seduction is never more evident than in the early stages of a relationship. I've lost count of the amount of men and woman that have visited me for 'extra special hair' or a sexy hair makeover, all because this is their chance to make the best impression on a first date. Enjoying a newly single status is another time when women decide to pull out all the stops and get sexy hair. Trying to improve their chances of attraction and desirability, the acquisition of a sexy, sassy new style could just be the key. It's actually happened to a client of mine – she literally walked out of the salon joking that if her new hair didn't get her a man, nothing would – only to be stopped by a hunky stranger telling her how stunning she was! Five years later, they are still happily married. Wow! Now that is the power of a great haircut!

hair colour

What's the first thing you notice about someone's hair? Chances are it will be the colour, whether dazzling blonde, gorgeous brunette or daring crimson. Colour like no other maketh the woman.

Throughout history those not content with their *natural hair colour* have been able to ENHANCE, DISGUISE and TRANSFORM their locks with artificial dyes, tints, herbs and minerals and have tried all manner of mixing and blending.

The first colourant properly marketed to the public came courtesy of Eugène Schueller in 1909 under the name L'Oréal. It was perfect timing – women were becoming experimental with hairstyles and fashion and were breaking free of the acceptable standards of the past. It was a time of liberation and L'Oréal have led the way in colour innovation and technology ever since. The phrase *'because you're worth it'* has become one of the most commonly used catchphrases and a byword for style.

Responses to hair colour can be fickle and depend on prevailing cultural attitudes, trends and celebrities – what's in one year is out the next. The morality of dyeing one's hair has been much debated and in some intellectual circles it has been frowned upon as mere 'vanity'. Over the years there has been much debate about the need to colour grey hair. In my opinion grey hair usually makes a woman look ten years older. And what's wrong with a bit of vanity? I was brought up to take pride in my appearance and the women I meet feel more confident and happier the better they look. Of course there are the obssesives for whom enough is never enough! If you ask me, all hair can benefit from a little colour enhancement. Hair without colour is like a face without make up. Grey hair is synonymous with ageing so why not indulge in a bit of luxury and relax at the salon with a little chitchat and a magazine whilst your colourless hair is given a new lease of life?

The colour barometer can swing to extremes. Natural blondeness is considered the height of beauty – princesses in fairytales nearly always have cascades of flowing golden locks, not to mention Barbie, Sindy and all the other dolls that little girls play with. Golden locks the colour of sunshine always bring forth gasps of delight. But when the blonde is 'fake' the negative associations can be huge; from bottle blonde to dumb blonde – how often have you heard (or used) the expression 'having a blonde moment'? All this, despite the fact that most of the world's most glamorous leading ladies have resorted to blonded locks at some time or another, laying testimony to how much favour blonde has.

"I'm not offended by dumb blonde jokes because I know that I'm not *dumb*. I also know that I'm not *blonde*."

DOLLY PARTON

With so much blonde inspiration from celebrities in the movie, music and entertainment words it's no wonder the 'blondes have more fun' expression appeared. And just as the world's leading women have become addicted to the blonde bottle so have the leading men from Beckham to Brad, Sting to Rod Stewart.

It goes without saying that for every gorgeous sex-kittenish blonde there's a sultry brunette – yes, brunettes can have fun too! Dark-haired beauties symbolize everything that is vampish, glamorous, bewitching and seductive and throughout history brunettes have transfixed us with their raven locks – the most famous of these temptresses being Cleopatra.

TO DYE FOR

Hair colour does have an undeserved bad reputation. The misconception is that using hair colour is damaging or bad because it's fake. There is a pressure on all of us to retain our youthful beauty. A youthful appearance implies vitality, optimism and even sex appeal – but beware, youthfulness can also work the other way since youth can imply a lack of experience or authority. Nonetheless ageing is something most of us fight and try to disguise. *10 Years Younger*, the makeover show on which I appear as the resident hair expert, shows us week after week that letting yourself go and stopping taking care of your appearance really does pile on the years. Radical surgery, new clothes and make up can work wonders but it's the hair that really does make the biggest impression.

Colouring hair is one of the easiest ways to fight back the years and can give a great boost to one's self-esteem.

There you go, I've said it, cosmetic, artificial hair colour can better what nature intended for you!

BE AWARE!

It is estimated that almost 70 percent of women in the UK colour their hair at some stage of their lives. The figure for men is nearer 10 percent but as many men are closet colourers the true figures are unknown. The benefits of colouring your hair far outweigh any physical damage to the hair or the time spent on it. There have been huge improvements to hair colour formulations over the decades and with safety being constantly monitored and patented technologies appearing all the time, colouring hair is safe to use as part of your beauty regime.

From time to time you do hear about some sensational stories about hair-colouring-gone-wrong. It's true that a very tiny percentage of people can develop a sensitivity to hair colour which may cause a reaction. The guidelines are simple: if you're concerned ask or do a patch test on your skin. If you are prone to a reaction it will appear very quickly, usually in the form of a rash, swelling or itching. Allergies can develop between colours so patch tests are recommended by all the leading hair colour manufacturers.

Recently there has been some scaremongering about a possible link between hair colourants and cancer. However, in studies conducted by the American Cancer Society and Harvard University it was concluded that the overall evidence excluded any appreciable and measurable risk of cancer from personal use of hair dyes. If you are at all in doubt or concerned, contact the manufacturer of the chosen hair colourant you or your hairdresser use.

Colour has the power to change a look instantly – even if you are doing it yourself. My stand on this is simple; if you are making a colour change leave it in the hands of the experts but if you are touching up the experts work then yes, it can be achieved at home.

Colour adds new dimension to your hair even if you stay similar to what you are naturally. Most woman want to go for something other than their natural hair colour and use colour to brighten, lighten or make their own colour more interesting. And for those who have never tried colour, trust me, even a few woven threads of colour placed around the face can make a huge difference – just like a slick of mascara can bring an eye to life.

Colour can brighten up dullness, add warmth, enhance the texture of the hair, make it look thicker and amazingly more alive. And if you're on a budget and want to colour without the salon price tag or can't face trying to do the back yourself at home (and all those stained towels), then I'll let you into a secret. Every local salon or hairdressing school needs willing volunteers so you could end up with a free colour – or at least at a fraction of the cost.

However, if you are in any doubt go to the salon for professional colour advice. It's really not worth the headache or hair ache to have a bad home job!

The mystery of home colouring kits starts with the picture of the girl on the front of the box all glorious flowing hair and just the colour you want. I hate to shatter your illusions and expose the work of the clever people in marketing but the chances are the picture will have been computer enhanced. The hair may actually be a wig or the colour may have been applied to bleached hair to get that really vibrant colour. Trust me, I've seen it happen. If you buy a box of honey blonde for instance, the chances of achieving the exact shade shown on the box are slim. Much depends on your natural hair colour. Home hair colour is complicated so be warned!

My advice would always be to consult your hairdresser on what your natural base colour is and what colour would suit you. You can only go darker or lighter a certain number of shades from your base colour.

So, 'what is base colour?' I hear you ask

Base colour is the natural hair shade you are born with, which may or may not lighten or darken as you get older. Reflect tone is the colour you see – for example, you may have a base colour of light brown with a reddish or coppery reflect tone. It is the reflect tone that makes hair so individual. Natural redheads still have a natural base colour but the reflect tone is much stronger and more obvious.

Hair colourists use a standard base level system of ten shades. Base 1 is black (think Elvis) and base 10 is lightest blonde (Marilyn Monroe). Everything else falls between the two (see opposite).

The irony is of course Monroe was naturally much darker and Presley naturally much lighter. We always want what we haven't got!

1   BLACK

3   DARK BROWN (US DARK BROWN)

4   MEDIUM BROWN (US BROWN)

5   LIGHT BROWN (US LIGHT BROWN)

6   DARK BLONDE (US DARK BLONDE)

7   MEDIUM BLONDE (US BLONDE)

8   LIGHT BLONDE (US LIGHT BLONDE)

9   VERY LIGHT BLONDE (US VERY LIGHT BLONDE)

10 LIGHTEST BLONDE (US LIGHTEST BLONDE)

I'm often asked 'what colour will suit me?' and each answer is UNIQUE. Colour experts the world over suggest colour is calculated through a consultation that takes into account skin tone, eye colour and the season as well as lifestyle, personality, the make up someone wears and how much time she is prepared to spend on it. *Phew!* It's a science all of its own. I often think it's about how much someone wants to whisper, talk or shout about their colour. For some women the phrase 'it looks really natural' is just what they want to hear while others are quite happy to tell the world that they've dyed and gone to heaven!

There are three main types of colourant:

Semi-permanent

This is just the lightest of all stains although be aware that regular use of semi-permanent dyes can lead to colour build-up occurs. The intensity of a semi lasts for up to six weeks and then the hair gradually fades back to its natural colour. Don't expect a good coverage of grey hair if over 25% of your hair has gone silver. Semis are great for the colour virgins or colour shy or those not up for a big commitment.

Permanent

This is a much deeper stain on the hair. The colour may fade a little but is generally fixed there until it the colour is cut out. You'll get a definite demarcation line where the new hair grows through so the roots require re-touching every 4–6 weeks to avoid the line. This type of hair colour will cover even the toughest of white hairs. Once you have used a permanent tint, nothing will lighten it except a bleaching agent so make sure you are happy with the colour first!

Lighteners

These usually contain a mixture of bleach and ammonia which lifts colour from your hair resulting in a lighter effect. Potentially this is the most damaging to hair but one of the most popular. Over 75% of the colour work that we do at my salon uses lighteners of some sort.

GO FOR IT!

From shocking one's parents as a teenager or paving the way to a new identity after a failed love, or simply enjoying something new, COLOUR is a way of life! I've spent years looking at why women love using colour to transform themselves. It's like having a whole new wardrobe courtesy of some foil and a tinting brush. I'm always amazed by how a woman's mood, spirit and energy is transformed after a good colour.

Going blonde can be addictive, as well as high-maintenance depending on the amount of blonding you choose. Whether it's sun-kissed highlights you're after or an all-over bleach job, think carefully about the blonde you want to be and how committed you are to maintaining your look.

If you have to go more than 5 base shades (see page 103) lighter to be the blonde you want to be, chances are you'll be fighting a losing battle so it's probably not for you! The best blondes are women who were blonde when they were children – the 'born blondes', if you like.

Your hair and skin should never be the same colour; if you have sallow skin avoid yellow tones and if you have pinkish skin avoid warm blonde tones. A good colourist can spot this pitfall with just an inch of regrowth but if you are using a home colour kit you're on your own.

Blonding looks most natural and more realistic when there are several tones through the hair rather than just one solid blonde colour.

'Blonderexia' (as we call it in the salon) is when a woman just doesn't know where to stop,

insisting on more, more, more! Less is often more in my opinion – my favourite blondes look gently sun-kissed.

If you decide to go an all-over blonde, think about whether you want to go for matching brows for a softer effect or whether you want to keep your brows dark for a more dramatic effect.

Blonde hair can certainly take a battering from day-to-day wear and tear, pollution and chlorine – swimming is a no-go for many blondes for fear of khaki hues.

Protection and TLC are the secret weapons in keeping your blonde hair looking good. Commit to weekly conditioning masks where the hair is pampered and nourished. Blonde hair does not reflect shine as easily as darker hair so a quality haircare regime is essential.

We all know there's nothing bland about being brown. Brunettes positively glow with shine and catch the light beautifully, resulting in a kaleidoscope effect of many tones. I often use foods to describe colour to clients when I'm creating a new look for them: milk or dark chocolate, frothy coffee, damson, plum, blackberry, shiraz, chestnut and all the colours of autumn are wonderful ways of describing colour. Forget the numbers, my colourists never talk numbers just gorgeous edibles!

If your skin is pale and you have blue eyes, jet-black hair can be ghostly and very ageing. Instead opt for a softer brown with warm tones.

Taking small baby steps can be a good way to try darker hair rather than going dramatically darker in one fell swoop. Subtler changes are often more flattering.

Going darker usually involves a semi-permanent or permanent colour. Look for products that include grapeseed oil in their ingredients list as this gives a stunning irridescent effect rather than a carpet-dyed effect.

Always take a strand test of hair from the back of your head before colouring. It may be that the auburn or chocolate you've always fancied being doesn't quite suit you.

A new darker colour will fade over a number of washes but if you feel it's too dark, resist the temptation to wash your hair over and over again – you won't do your hair any favours. Wait at least a few days to get used to seeing your new look in the mirror and then, if you're really not happy, visit your hairdresser who can come up with some quick fixes.

Use pictures to describe colour. One person's mahogany is another's purple and there is definitely more confusion when it comes to the vast shade of brunettes.

Visit a beauty counter after a new dye job, as your make up bag will probably need a make over too!

HIDING ROOTS TIPS

Whether you are blonde or brunette, pink, blue, crimson or flaming copper there are loads of quick fixes and tips to disguise roots and freshen up your colour between salon visits.

Match a mascara to your chosen colour and brush it on for a quick temporary paint job.

Wear hairstyles that frame the face or have texture or waves to disguise undyed roots.

AVOID RULER STRAIGHT PARTINGS; FLIPPING AND CHANGING PARTINGS IS A BRILLIANT DISGUISE.

Dry shampoos can stop the hair looking flat and reduce the tell-tale signs of roots that need touching up.

Ask for a few woven threads of different colour around the face and especially at the parting for a softer regrowth area.

Don't try to hide your hair by scraping it into a ponytail – this will only make the roots more obvious.

Have a quick 'T section' touch-up job to cover the hairline and parting between colours.

Modern colourants very often have conditioning properties but coloured hair does need extra care. Use deep conditioning masks at least once a week.

COLOURING TIPS

If you're thinking about a big colour change visit the wig department of a department store or specialist wig shop and try on a wig the colour you love.

If you can't afford salon colour regularly, aim to a visit a salon at least once a year for a colour overall.

If your hair is weak and damaged apply a deep conditioning repair treatment to the tips of the hair before applying to the roots. Leave it on whilst colouring the remaining hair.

DON'T USE YOUR FAVOURITE FLUFFY WHITE TOWELS – IT'S MUCH BETTER TO USE OLD ONES TO MOP UP SPLASHES AND SPILLS.

APPLY A SLICK OF VASELINE AROUND THE HAIRLINE TO AVOID SKIN STAINING.

Always stick to the devclopment time – use a timer to make sure you don't leave the dye on too long.

Always read the label – you'd be surprised how many disasters could be avoided.

Always use the gloves in your home colouring kit – stained hands and fingernails are a no-no!

Get a friend to help, especially at the back. Alternatively, use a 3-way mirror so you can see what you are doing to the back of your head.

Finally, if home hair colour goes wrong don't panic and DEFINITELY don't pick up those kitchen scissors! Another mistake people often make is to rush out and buy another packet of dye. Instead consult the manufacturer's helpline – it should be clearly marked on the instruction leaflet.

HAIR COLOURING TIMETABLE

Follow this hair colouring timetable to get the best from colouring, either at home or at the hairdressers.

7 days before use a hair mask. This will heal the weak hair and strengthen the hair ready for the colour chemicals.

On the day whether you have an appointment at the salon or whether you are doing it at home, make time for your colour. Don't feel rushed – good colouring can't be done in a hurry. Arrive on time at the salon.

Don't shampoo just before colouring. The natural oils that are secreted will protect and hydrate the scalp during the colouring process and avoid sensitivity.

Rebook your next colour appointment as you leave the salon to make sure you can get in at the time you want and with the colourist you trust!

1–2 days after colouring to preserve your colour try waiting a couple of days before shampooing. Expect to see some residue of colour in the shower on the first wash. You should use a shampoo and conditioner designed to look after your coloured hair.

7 days after colouring use a deep conditioning mask once every week to preserve and protect your colour, as well as build the quality. The conditioning agents in colours will wear off after about 5–7 washes.

GREYING, greying, *gone!*

For those that have moved over to the grey side – I say move back! Grey hair can make you look washed out, pale and faded. Grey hair absorbs light and generally looks flat and dull. The texture can often be coarse and frizzy.

The day we notice our first grey hair (it's actually white hair there's no such thing as a grey hair) can be quite a shock. For most people grey hair hits in the prime of life although for many men and women the greying process starts earlier – sometimes even in late teens. Nature plays a cruel trick and robs the hair of melanin (the substance that gives hair its colour). And what makes it worse is that grey hair often goes hand in hand with the first wrinkles or the slightly expanding waistline – it's no wonder that most woman hit the bottle and never stop from that point on. Anything but grey hair!

However, there are scores of women out there who don't want the hassle of maintaining a hair colour and would rather 'grow old gracefully'. Women who resist the bottle and still look good are usually those who are genetically blessed, have a chic demeanour with striking eyes and looks, fabulous skin, great figures and would look good

whatever their hair colour. But for those who are less fortunate, grey hair can be a serious no-no.

When hair colour is put back into grey hair it automatically makes hair look shinier, healthier and younger. Grey hair really does drain colour from the face and a few strands of coloured hair next to the skin can make a huge difference. There are plenty of options, from low lights to highlights to total coverage but in my opinion, hair with colour is definitely better than hair without colour.

BLONDES!

In the melting pot of genes caused by world migration and the evolution of mankind, the natural blonde is ultimately a dying breed and will be superseded by darker-haired, darker-skinned races.

But thanks to chemistry rather than parentage the blonde goddess will never leave the catwalk, cinema screen, celebrity magazines or indeed your very own hair identity.

As far back as Roman times blonde hair has been the subject of fascination. Historically, natural blonde hair is associated with Nordic heritage. From Roman to Venetian and Renaissance art, and in more recent times, the golden vamps of Hollywood and bottle-blonde rock stars, blondes have ruled the colour charts, symbolizing effervescence and youthfulness. Marilyn Monroe would not be the same without her blonde 'do' and now she lives on eternally as the patron saint of peroxide.

Women have always been dissatisfied with hair colour and history shows us time and time again how people have experimented with hair lightening, from the ancient Egyptians to the Greeks, Hebrews, Persians and Chinese.

Golden hair tumbles through just about every fairytale and bedtime story, from Rapunzel to Alice In Wonderland to Cinderella. It's no wonder we are all fascinated by blondes.

Blonde has a language all of its own and can be powerful, cool, brash, innocent, fragile, dizzy, raunchy and glamorous. The female stars of Hitchcock and Bond movies are littered with blondes, and the worlds of music, art and fashion are inhabited by any number of blondes, from sex kittens to fashion queens, power blondes and blonde icons. *Blonde ambition is it!*

The blonde may well be the subject of a million dumb blonde jokes, and style commentators may think blonde cheap but any blonde backlash is only ever temporary. In surveys 59% of women said they'd prefer to be blonde and those that kick the habit keep going back. Those that try a few strands always cry for more – it's like a drug! Blondes comes in all sizes, the sophisticated blonde, the glamorous blonde, the Ibiza sun-kissed blonde, the power blonde, trailer trash blonde or Swedish porn star blonde – there is a blonde for everyone!

REDHEADS

Red hair varies from a deep orange to a pale copper. The palest red hair is often referred to as strawberry blonde – I have to confess this description beats me! As I mentioned earlier, red hair is characterized by high levels of red-coloured reflect pigment and lower levels of the darker base pigments. Natural red hair is usually complemented by fair skin and freckles and without any evidence natural redheads are portrayed has having fiery tempers! I'm not sure if this is true, *although I must admit I have met some pretty fiery redheads!*

Natural redheads are pretty special – only a very small percentage of the world's population are blessed with this rarest of all natural colours! In the United States just 6% of the population have red hair while in Scotland and Ireland the figures are more like 13% and 10% respectively. Obviously the reason for these percentages is based on the global population shifts that have happened over thousands of years.

What many people don't realize is that the red hair gene can skip generations and can turn up out of the blue three, four or even five generations later. On men it often appears in facial hair but nowhere else.

Throughout the centuries redheads have been revered and feared, adorned and adored, from Queen Boadicea, Mary Magdalene, Queen Elizabeth the First, and any number of pre Raphaelite beauties. The colour Titian takes its name from the artist of the same name who immortalized red-haired women in his paintings.

Natural redheads may have to put up with the teasing and the 'ginger' jokes but there's no denying just how striking, colourful and desired red hair can be. As far as transforming yourself into a redhead cosmetically is concerned – why not? Many natural redheads would question the wisdom of this as there are plenty out there who dye their hair the other way. But if fiery locks is what you want, the most important thing you should consider is whether it will work with your skin tone. Most natural redheads have pale skin and green or blue eyes so if you are olive-skinned or over tanned it can look a little odd. Red colour can be applied in all manner of shades and techniques from the palest, subtlest glow to the brightest of fires. Red hair does tend to have fantastic shine and can be a real show stopper!

The 3 *secrets* to GREAT colour

BESPOKE COLOUR Just like a great chef, a good colourist will tweak and mix a formula that is unique to you, changing the ingredients and amounts to suit you at that time. When your colourist says 'same as last time?' it's time to change your colourist. They should be creating the perfect shade for where your hair is at right now. If the same colour is applied time and time again it will either get darker or lighter. The other key thing is that a good colourist will rarely mix up just one shade – three, four or even five shades make the perfect bespoke colour. This is where a hairdresser wins hands down over a box of dye.

TECHNIQUE If you are applying home colour always start at the back of the head. Heat rises and the hair on top of the head develops more quickly than the hair at the nape of the neck. A good colourist will colour the hair section by section, often working out what to do where and using several different techniques. Again, these techniques can't be found on the back of a box.

CHANGE If you apply the same colour over a period of time you will get a build-up. You may not notice it yourself but take pictures of your hair colour every six months to chart the change. The biggest mistake most woman make (especially in the war against anti-ageing) is sticking to the same hair colour for years. Gently tweaking and changing your hair colour as you get older is the secret. There are times when you should go lighter: if you are naturally dark lifting the colour a few shades lighter can work wonders (my mother lightened her raven black locks to a soft medium brown as she matured). The reverse is true for natural blondes – they actually need to add more depth to their blonde hair. And for those that sit in the middle of the base colour scale soft chestnut, subtle copper and toffee blonde shades all look stunning as a woman gets older.

IF

YOUR BLONDE HAIR IS LOOKING A LITTLE BRASSY, TARNISHED OR GREEN THEN TRY THIS LITTLE TRICK. CRUSH THREE ASPIRIN INTO A COUPLE OF TABLESPOONS OF WATER AND MIX INTO A PASTE. APPLY THE PASTE TO THE HAIR AND LEAVE ON FOR FIVE MINUTES BEFORE RINSING OFF. YOU'LL BE AMAZED AT HOW MUCH FRESHER YOUR HAIR LOOKS.

HAIR *and*
anti-ageing

Can you make your hair and yourself look younger? Oh, yes you can! Many of you know as me the makeover guru on the hit TV show *10 Years Younger* now exported around the world. The TV show aims to take at lest ten years off a volunteer's age, as polled by members of the public. I guess you, like me, have screamed with delight as the volunteer is revealed in front of the revolving mirror and is rendered speechless when she sees a new, younger version of herself.

Over the years that we have brought makeover magic into your living room I'm always overwhelmed when people say *'it's all about the hair'*.

I guess I'm biased but I agree! It's true that the right hair can dramatically knock off the years. And despite my huge respect for my fellow experts – the fashion stylist, the make up artist, cosmetic dentist and surgeon – when that mirror turns around it's usually always the hair that makes everyone go WOW! Hair has that wonderful ability to amaze people and, without doubt, can make someone look and feel younger!

So whether you are a twenty-something party animal, a thirty-something woman juggling a hectic career and family, getting used to being forty, hitting the menopause in your fifties or embracing retirement in your sixties, the secret to looking young and gorgeous is – yes, you guessed it – hair! If I've it heard once I've heard it a million times: if your hair looks good, nothing else matters. Of course, ageing is inevitable and the aim of this chapter is to share some secrets on how to knock off the years.

Follow these simple 'lifestyle' guidelines and you will start to see your hair take on new energy and recapture some its youth.

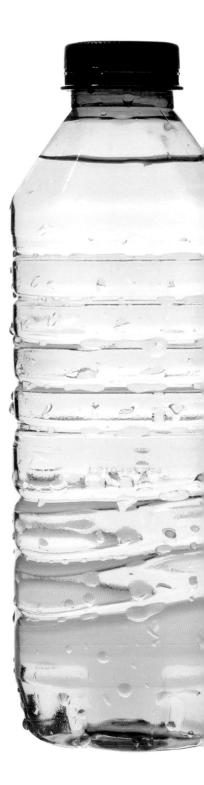

Eat fresh fruit and vegetables. We all know that we should be eating at least five portions a day to make sure we get enough vitamins and minerals in our diets – and this applies to anti-ageing as well. I know it's boring, but it works!

Eating the right things is all very well but you need to make sure you also drink plenty of water. And water really is the key here – tea, coffee and alcohol won't do it! Hydration is essential for all aspects of body health and is the secret to youthful hair that is full of vitality. As we age, we lose more and more moisture, resulting in drier, weaker, brittle hair, so putting back the moisture is essential. Drink up to two litres a day, avoid sugary drinks and lower your alcohol consumption and your hair will soon show its gratitude, you'll see!

Avoid crash diets which can actually affect the health of your hair. Instead adopt a lifestyle where your diet is rich in anti-oxidants such as vitamins A, C and E and eat carotenes to fight the effects of ageing free radicals. Consult a nutritionist or health food store for more advice.

Maintaining the hair's STRENGTH, LUSTRE and VITALITY Is the secret to youthful looks and one that most of the world's leading beauties practise. Be warned: like skin, hair starts its slippery journey into old age surprisingly early. It's perfectly normal and natural for your hair to change over the years, losing some of its vitality. We all see it happening with our complexions as lines and wrinkles appear – the changes are much more noticeable. In hair it is less obvious. But undoubtedly there will be loss of shine, with hair becoming less manageable, harder to hold a style and generally lacking energy. These are all the symptoms of the ageing process. Drugs, pollution, oral contraceptives, medication, stress and poor diets all add to the ageing process.

How do you know your hair is ageing? Technically your hair is not actually **ageing**, it's not that the hair is getting **older**, it's just that as we age the hair doesn't grow as quickly or for as long and so it often feels and looks thinner, or it doesn't swing or bounce like it used to. Mature clients are always asking me to *'put some life back into my hair'* and of course there is the change in colour as those pesky grey hairs sneak through. Is there any hope, I hear you ask? Yes! A good stylist can cut, shape and style away the years.

In chapter 2 I discussed the positive effects of a diet rich in oily fish – tuna, sardines, mackerel and salmon really are good for your hair. Not only do they guard against inherited problems such as heart disease, arthritis and osteoporosis but are fantastic for maintaining the hair's vitality. You are probably thinking does it really matter what I eat? Just tell me which style I should wear to knock off the years! I'm afraid it's not that simple. The right hairstyle is like the right pair of jeans – it's different for everyone and can be hard to pin down but once you've found it, nothing can stop you! But, ultimately, youthful hair is all about vitality and health. I learnt this as a young hairdresser and have offered advice to my clients ever since as I believe that hair health is essential to a good hairstyle, in the same way that the best garments are made from great fabric. I started my career wanting to be a fashion designer, and you could say this is exactly what I have become – I just work with a different fabric. If a client brings a rough bit of hessian for me to design with the creation is never as good as the finest silk. By feeding your body correctly you have more chance of shiny happy hair.

I STARTED MY CAREER WANTING TO BE A FASHION DESIGNER, AND YOU COULD SAY THIS IS EXACTLY WHAT I HAVE BECOME, – I JUST WORK WITH A DIFFERENT FABRIC

However, it's not just about protein. A balanced diet rich in fibre is essential too. I know you don't need me to tell you what foods are good and bad but whole grains, fruit and vegetables all help to balance hormones. The changes in hormones as we age certainly affects hair's vitality and manageability. So whether this advice is right for you right now in your life, or whether you share it with your mum, auntie, colleague, sister or friend, one thing is for sure: you know a little bit more about how to get more from your hair.

Good nutrition balanced with regular exercise will reward your body, mind and soul as well as your skin and energy levels in so many positive ways – none more so than glossy, **_shiny happy hair!_**

So a diet rich in protein and fibre is good for your hair but without good fats hair, like skin, can look sluggish, dull and lifeless. The top choices for healthy good fats in your balanced diet include:

OLIVE OIL Always look for extra-virgin cold-pressed varieties as they have the highest nutritional value and help your body absorb anti-oxidant vitamins A and E which will help your hair to shine.

SESAME OIL This is a brilliant source of vitamins B and E and is yummy added to salads.

WALNUT OIL This can replace other bad fats in baking and is also rich in anti-oxidants vital to hair growth and health.

NUTS AND SEEDS
Great for snacking and sprinkling onto salads and sandwiches. They not only add flavour and texture but are a fantastic beauty secret for boosting your hair's health and vitality. Try walnuts, almonds, pine nuts, pecans, sunflower and pumpkin seeds.

So, enough about diet. The facts are there in black and white and the sooner you follow my advice, the sooner you will have youthful hair full of vitality.

Shiny curtains of flowing hair, a head full of voluptuous curls, bouncy hair that doesn't split at the tips – these are all the signs of healthy hair that looks good and helps you to look younger. However, over the years hair will show the signs of age: dullness, breakage and thinning. And left alone, these signs will get steadily worse. Of course hair is already dead but that doesn't mean it's not affected by the passage of time. As we age the body's cells don't replace quite as quickly and so the active cells around the hair follicle are not as strong, resulting in hair that is finer, duller and weaker.

But don't despair – there are solutions in the form of hair products. Many of these simply moisturize the hair fibre, making the hair look and feel stronger. Advances in shampoo alone, where complex blends of proteins, moisturizers and amino acids are mixed together, really make a big difference in the anti-ageing war!

So do these 'anti-ageing' hair care products work? Yes, is the simple answer. With their complex blends of proteins, silicones and voluminizers,

they all work by realigning the cuticle scales making the hair look and feel smoother, shinier and therefore younger. For many women losing hair density is their biggest fear. Unlike men who lose it around the temples or the crown area, generally woman lose a percentage of hair all over the head and particularly right on the top – usually where they notice it most in the mirror. I've met women who have tried everything in their power to reverse the natural process that their body may be going through, while

other women are happy to just let nature take its course. Hair loss can be devastating and embarrassing and can lead to loss of self esteem or pride. Times have changed and women are now much more comfortable talking about this issue that effects an alarmingly high percentage of women. There is more advice and more solutions and remedies available that may help. There are no guaranteed solutions as there are so many complex and diverse reasons for hair loss, ranging from stress, medication, oral contraceptive use, hormone imbalances, weight gain, thyroid problems and, of course, genetics. For this reason I always refer clients who suffer with hair loss to a doctor or trichologist who can best assess the possible reasons and solutions. The next step is to visit a good stylist who can cut and style hair that has lost some of its density to create the right look for you and give you **Shiny Happy Hair**.

How to look YOUNGER...

1 Never hang onto the same style for too long. Fashions change and so should your hairstyle. You should change or adapt your look at least every three years or you run the risk of looking like you are living in another decade which can dramatically age you. It doesn't have to be a drastic change – it could just be a change of parting or adding or reducing width or height.

2 **Avoid overly trendy haircuts or conceptual dramatic haircuts. Over a certain age it just looks like you are trying too hard. You may love wearing conceptual clothes and if that's the case just keep the hair simple and tailored.**

3 Avoid wearing haircuts with hard, sharp, dramatic angles or anything too directional – leave this look to the kids! I'm not saying you can't be fashionable but over 40 chic is the way, not gimmick!

4 Centre partings are generally not flattering even on a teenager so avoid them at all costs. Casual partings are much more flattering as a woman ages.

5 *Gentle backcombing can add a little oomph to fine thin hair but hair that is obviously backcombed is a definite no-no! You don't want to end up looking like the barmaid in your favourite TV soap or like you're still living in the sixties.*

6 I'm constantly asked whether I agree that women over forty should chop off their long hair to give a more youthful appearance. I believe a woman should feel confident, sexy and attractive and if that means having long hair then the answer is no! But it does have to be in great condition, have fabulous colour and be cut into a flattering shape. No-one who has past their teens can get away with hair hanging from a centre parting like a pair of curtains.

7 Avoid haircuts that are too severe and short. A crop can look great on a mature woman but wear it soft and ask your stylist to cut it in such a way that the edges look a little outgrown. There's nothing worse for adding on the years than hard, neat lines around the face.

8 *My pet hate is hair that looks like it can't move, fixed in place within an inch of its life. If you want hold, look for hairsprays that offer flexible hold. Hair should be free and soft and have movement, not look like a helmet or lampshade.*

9 If you are using colour all over your hair, opt for multi-dimensional tints that are light-reflective. The least flattering of hair tints are matt and solid.

my top 20 dos and don'ts

I'm a great advocate of colour and most of the women that visit my salons wear some kind of colour, whether it's a full head tint, where the colourist mixes many colours together to get a unique blend, or just a few delicately woven flickers of colour around the face. Colour adds life to hair – think of it as an overall investment in your beauty regime and you'll always keep the years at bay.

Use styling products to enhance the texture in your hair. You are looking to add shine or polish but not glue your hair together. There is nothing worse than hair that looks artificial.

A little volume is flattering as a woman ages. Avoid straight, flat hair and use heated appliances to help you achieve body, bounce, curls or waves.

Ask your stylist to cut the tips of your hair with the tips of the scissors rather than the length of the blade. This will give you a softer effect, whatever shape you wear. Hair that is ruffled, softly textured and loose is much more flattering on a woman over forty.

Regular daily scalp massages for a few minutes as you shower in the morning and before you go to sleep can really help the blood supply to the hair follicles, encouraging healthy hair growth.

Sleeping on silk pillowcases is very kind to your hair and reduces the snags and tears that happen as your hair moves around the pillow during your sleep. This is a good tip for keeping skin smooth too.

Wearing hair tied up can be very feminine and look pretty but avoid scraping it back severely. Instead pull it back into a looser style and wear subtle hair accessories. Spraying a dry shampoo through the hair before loosely pulling the hair back with the fingers and securing is much softer.

Taking a few extra minutes each day to style your hair can make a real difference. A lot of women just don't bother, but using a heated roller brush, even if you don't blow-dry your hair, can have great results. If you are really lazy, just do the top sections and the front and let the rest of your hair kick and bend. Use a light serum to polish away any stray hairs. Frizzy, unkempt hair is one of the worst ageing culprits.

Have at least three or four haircuts a year. With age the hair does get weaker and thinner and therefore the tips split more easily. Avoid split ends at all costs.

Be religious about using deep conditioning treatments. Used in conjunction with a healthy balanced diet, deep-conditioning masks will add moisture – the essential secret weapon for anti-ageing.

It's okay to use pictures of hairstyles you like but try to be realistic about what you and your stylist can achieve.

Get the
LOOK

Hair fashions come and go but there are some classic styles that never date. In this chapter I show you how easy it is to change your look from day to night and back again. Hair should be playful and versatile and experimenting with your hair is just like trying out some new heels or changing the length of your skirt. There are 10 fantastic looks here, showing that fabulous hair doesn't necessarily mean booking in to see a top stylist. All these hairstyles can be done at home with just a few of the right tools and products. Pick your favourite and go for it!

The **10** LOOKS

Super Sleek, *page 132*

Catwork Ponytail, *page 136*

Ballerina Bun, *page 140*

Smooth Operator, *page 144*

Red Carpet Glitz, *page 148*

Quiff It Up, *page 152*

Bohemian Chic, *page 156*

Retro Glamour, *page 160*

The Hepburn, *page 164*

Beach Babe, *page 168*

LOOK 1

Super Sleek

What you need:
Comb
Styling mousse (medium hold)
Cushion hairbrush
Hairdryer and nozzle
Heat protective spray
Straightening irons
Shine serum

Super Sleek is the ultimate it girl look – high on drama, sexy yet sweet it shines like a star and can be worn with everything from casual to classic, uptown to downtown. The steps that follow can apply to hair of various lengths; here I have worked with shorter hair. Easy to achieve, this look ticks all the boxes on the style stakes.

"Super sleek means super sexy"

1 Start with clean, wet hair that you have squeezed dry with a towel. Comb through to get rid of any tangles. Apply mousse to a brush or comb before applying it to the hair. This will ensure that you get an even application of mousse.

2 Use a cushion brush and hairdryer to dry the hair. Move the hair around the head, brushing from side to side to achieve gentle root lift.

3 The cushion brush can also be used to smooth the hair and turn it under.

4 For that super sleek look you will need to smooth the hair with professional quality straightening irons. Spritz the hair with a heat protective spray and use clips to section the hair as you work on each area. As always, take care not to go over the same area to avoid heat damage. Finally, use a shine serum for a glossy polish.

LOOK 2

Catwalk Ponytail

What you need:
Round brush
Hairdryer and nozzle
Styling mousse (medium hold)
Bristle brush
No-snag hairband
Kirby grips
Hairspray (medium to strong hold)
Large-barrelled curling tongs
Shine serum

There isn't a fashion show where I've styled where the ponytail hasn't graced the runway. It's the perfect fashionista look and graces the pages of all the top fashion and beauty titles. Worn high or low, messy or super neat, it can add glamour and glitz to even the dullest hair. It's also a secret weapon for bad hair days. Here I have dressed the pony high and jaunty so the hair has some bounce. If you have skinny hair try adding a few clip-in hair extensions before creating the ponytail as this will add bulk.

"Sometimes the simplest hairstyles are the most stunning"

1

For best results the hair should be freshly washed and blow-dried using a round brush and a small amount of styling mousse. Then, using a bristle brush, bring all the hair back to the back of the head and gather in the opposite hand. Continue brushing the hair until all the hair is in place then secure with a no-snag hairband.

2

Take a small section of hair from the ponytail and wrap it around the base of the ponytail to cover the no-snag hairband. Use kirby grips to secure this in place. A hairspray can be used to smooth away any stray hairs.

3

For extra bounce or waves, use large-barrelled tongs randomly through the ponytail. To create a voluminous ponytail use a bristle brush to tease the hair at the root area of the ponytail. Work in sections and make sure the top section is smoothed over so that all the teasing is not seen. Finish with hairspray for hold and smooth over a tiny amount of shine serum.

LOOK 3

Ballerina **Bun**

What you need:
Round hairbrush
Hairdryer and nozzle
Styling mousse (medium hold)
Comb
No-snag hairband
Bristle hairbrush
Hairspray (medium to strong hold)
Kirby grips

Romantic and glamorous, this look is stunning and elegant and would work perfectly for a gorgeous night out. It looks great worn with a cocktail dress or evening gown but would work just as well with a great pair of jeans and killer heels. Worn to one side it is pretty, girly and totally feminine. The secret for hair up is to secure the hair out of the way so you are free to play and flaunt your lovely style.

"A stunning look that is soft and romantic"

1

For best results first wash and blow-dry the hair smooth using a round brush and mousse. Create a side parting with a comb then, using your hands, gather all the hair over to the opposite side of the head behind the ear area to create a ponytail. Use a no-snag hairband to secure.

2

Use your fingers to pinch random pieces through the top section to create more volume and texture.

3

Using a bristle brush, backcomb the ponytail in sections. Smooth over the top section gently with the bristle brush and apply hairspray for hold.

4

Twist the ponytail around and wrap in a clockwise direction tucking the ends under the bun. Hold in place with your hands.

5

When the desired shape is in place use kirby grips to secure. Hairspray should be used to give hold and final polish to the shape.

LOOK 4

SMOOTH OPERATOR

What you need:
Smoothing product
Comb
Hairdryer
Large round brush
Straightening irons
Shine serum

One of the must-have look of today – shiny, healthy and fabulous. The hair looks and feels like silk and perfectly accompanies any fabric or cut of clothes. It screams that you care about your hair and has all the hallmarks of shiny happy hair. Worn from a central or side parting it's a favourite of many a celebrity and is much admired!

"Smooth and sophisticated – and perfect shine"

For best results start with freshly washed and conditioned hair. Apply a smoothing product and use your fingers to help spread the product evenly through the hair. Use a comb to part the hair in the centre.

Blow-dry the hair, starting at the back of the head. Work through the hair section by section, using a large round brush and a hairdryer to lift the hair at the roots and smooth through the rest of the hair until complete.

For final polish and shine use straightening irons throughout the hair. Work in sections, smoothing the hair from root to tip. Take care not to go over the same area to avoid heat damage. Finally use a few drops of shine serum and apply gently to the hair, avoiding the root area.

LOOK 5

Red Carpet GLITZ

What you need:
Large round hairbrush
Styling mousse (medium hold)
Clips or Kirby grips
Hairdryer and nozzle
Large-barrelled tongs
Bristle hairbrush
Hairspray (medium hold)
Shine serum

Perfect for those special occasions this utterly fabulous hair screams glamour. Worn with a diagonal parting it's totally head-turning stuff. Perfect for any girl who has long hair, whether shoulder length or longer. Blonde or brunette you'll wear this style with pride.

"Utterly fabulous hair that screams glamour"

1 Start with freshly washed and conditioned hair. Apply mousse to a brush and apply evenly throughout the hair. For long thick hair, it is probably best to section and clip the hair. Starting at the back of the head, take a section of hair and blow-dry using a large round brush and hairdryer. Lift the hair at the roots and curl the hair around the brush until dry. While the section is still warm, loop the hair and use clips to secure. Allow the hair to completely cool before removing the clips.

2 Tong sections in the same direction with large-barrelled tongs to create extra curl and movement.

3 Use a bristle brush and your fingers to smooth out the curls and reduce separation until the desired result is achieved. Use hairspray to hold and a shine serum for polish.

Alternative:
Big on Volume
Turn your head upside down and use your hands to shake out the curls from the roots to the ends. Once upright arrange the hair with your hands and use hairspray to hold in place.

LOOK 6

Quiff It UP

What you need:
Comb
Hairbrush
Styling mousse (medium to strong hold)
Hairdryer and nozzle
Round hairbrush
Hairspray (medium to strong hold)

From punk and rock goddess to glamorous starlet, lifting hair off the face always gets the right sort of attention. For tiny frames it can add inches and for fuller faces it can take off the pounds. A favourite of the catwalk it's the ultimate in cool and is perfect for day or night. It's a classic style that always looks bang on trend.

"Anything is possible with this look!"

1 Start with clean, wet hair that you have squeezed dry with a towel. Comb through to get rid of any tangles. Apply mousse to a brush or comb before applying it to the hair. This will ensure that you get an even application of mousse.

2 Use a professional hairdryer and your fingers to blast dry the hair. You want plenty of root lift and texture.

3 Use a round brush through the front fringe area to create root lift and a bend through the hair. Make sure you allow the hair to cool before removing the brush.

4 Finally, use the hairdryer and a hairspray together to create root lift and hold for the texture created. Sweep the hair into the quiff that you want and use more hairspray to hold it in place.

LOOK 7

Bohemian Chic

What you need:
Round hairbrush
Hairdryer and nozzle
Styling mousse (medium hold)
Hairspray (medium to strong hold)
Large-barrelled tongs
Comb
No-snag hairband
Kirby grips

This is a gorgeous feminine style that adds fullness and body to hair. Its slightly messy texture lends itself well to city living or party time. Adding height to those with a small frame and softening the overall look of a larger frame it's a fabulous, casual, not-too-done look that can transform longer lengths of hair. Accessorize with flowers for a wedding or special occasion or glam it up with sparkly clips or combs for a party.

"Sometimes messy is best"

For best results first wash and blow-dry the hair using a round brush and mousse. Take sections through the hair and spray each section with hairspray first then use large-barrelled tongs through the mid-lengths and ends.

Use a comb to create a side parting and then through the fringe area place a small three-strand plait by alternately moving the side strands into the middle until all the hair is used. Secure with a no-snag hairband at the end.

Starting at the crown area take random sections of hair and use your fingers to tease the hair by running them over the hair from the tips to the roots.

Gather up each section using your fingers then twist all of the section from the roots to the ends.

Wrap the section around your fingers to create a knot effect then use kirby grips to secure in place on the head. Repeat with all the sections throughout the rest of the hair until complete. Then use a couple of kirby grips to pin the plait back in between the knots. Finish with hairspray.

LOOK 8

Retro Glamour

What you need:
Round hairbrush
Hairdryer and nozzle
Comb
Heat protective spray
Medium-sized Velcro rollers
Kirby grips
Diffuser attachment
Hairspray (medium hold)

Inspired by a bygone era of Hollywood vamps, this look is sexy, flirty and altogether gorgeous. It adds drama to daring outfits with its volume and for those who love to look like they've just stepped out of the salon, it's the ultimate in high maintenance chic. Worn to a party, it's guaranteed to turn heads.

"Vampish and flirty – this look will turn heads!"

1

For best results wash and dry the hair, leaving it slightly damp. Comb the hair into sections and spray each with a heat protective spray. Roll the sections of hair into Velcro rollers and use kirby grips to secure.

2

Use a hairdryer with a diffuser attachment to finish off the drying process. This will take approximately 10–20 minutes, depending on the thickness of the hair. Allow the hair to cool completely before removing the rollers.

3

Use your fingers to comb out the curls until the desired result is achieved. Finish with hairspray to hold in place.

LOOK 9

The HEPBURN

What you need:
Round hairbrush
Hairdryer and nozzle
Styling mousse (medium hold)
Bristle hairbrush
No-snag hairband
Wide-toothed comb
Hairspray (medium to strong hold)
Kirby grips

Inspired by the classic chic of Hollywood starlet Audrey Hepburn, this stunning topknot is perfect from dawn till dusk. High on the drama stakes, it is glamorous, beautiful and all-and-all-out classic. It will add inches to a smaller frame and should be worn further back on the head for the tall girls. Don't save it just for special occasions but add wow factor to even the most casual of days with stunningly gorgeous hair.

"Classic Hollywood glamour"

For best results first wash and blow-dry the hair using a round brush and mousse. Then using a bristle brush, bring all the hair back to the crown of the head and gather in the opposite hand. Keep brushing until all the hair is in place then secure with a no-snag hairband. Divide the ponytail into four equal sections.

Take each section and using a wide-toothed comb, backcomb from the roots to the ends.

Smooth over the top of each section with a bristle brush and apply a spritz of hairspray to the section. Use your fingers to smooth over any stray hairs.

Loop the section over your fingers and arrange near to the base of the ponytail. Each section should loop a couple of times.

Once each section is in place use kirby grips to secure: one for the first loop and one for the second loop. Repeat for each section, taking care to build the shape of the hairstyle by looping loops on top of each other. Use hairspray to add final polish and hold.

LOOK 10

Beach Babe

What you need:
Medium hold mousse
Smoothing cream
Hairdryer and diffuser attachment
Triple-barrelled waver
Shine serum

Beach babe or city girl – this look is young, fresh and easy. Casual and relaxed but high on the sexy hit list, it's hot! This can be worn by anyone with mid-length hair or longer – and it's really versatile. Try holding the hair back off the face with a beaded or sequined hair clip and change the parting from central to side, depending on your face shape.

"This look is young, fresh and relaxed – perfect for casual summer days"

1 Mix together a mousse and a smoothing cream and apply to washed and conditioned hair. Take medium-sized sections of the hair and twist them with your fingers from the roots to the tips.

2 Blow-dry the hair, starting at the back of the head. Work through the hair section by section using the diffuser attachment to lift the hair at the roots. Continue until all the hair is dry.

3 Use a triple-barrelled waver to create more definition. Similar to a crimper (but with bigger plates), it makes perfect 'beach' waves. Use a shine serum throughout the hair and at the tips.

INDEX